THE ART OF DIRECTION

THE ART OF DIRECTION

A Guide for Parents

How to Help Your Child
Overcome Imbalances of All Kinds

Duncan Gill, MD, and Joseph R. Walsh, LCMHC

ISBN: 978-1-7346257-0-7

CONTENTS

About This Book ix

A Brief Introduction to the Authors xi

Who Are These Guys, Anyway? xiii

Part 1: Goals, Imbalances, and How We Can Help ... 1

    How We Define Success 3
    Imbalances: Obstacles to Good Functioning 7
    Responding to Imbalances: Where Should Parents Start? ... 13

Part 2: Biological Imbalances 17

    The Straight Dope on Psychiatry 19
    Susan: The Case for Medication 21
    Where Psychiatry Fits In 23
    Psychiatric Diagnosis 27
    Psychopharmacology 101 35
    A Few Common Myths about Psychiatric Medication ... 39

Part 3: Behavioral Imbalances 43

    An Introduction to Wholeistic Education 45
    What Is Wholeistic Education? 47
    Basic Principles: Habits and Groups 51
    Mike: The Magic of a Healthy Culture 55
    How Wholeistic Education Creates Healthy Groups ... 57
    The Three Educator Objectives and Three Educator Challenges ... 61
    Jordan: Modeling Healthy Relationships 67
    Tom: Avoiding Adversarial Dynamic 69
    WED's Social Code: The Behavioral Guidelines ... 71
    The Behavioral Guidelines 73
    Commitment to the Guidelines and Restriction ... 77

The Four Rs   81
What Are the Four Rs?   83
An Example of the Four Rs: WED in Action   85
Kate: Providing Clear Reflection   91
Wholeistic Education Summary   93
Applying Wholeistic Education at Home   95
The Foundation of Your Home: Safety   99
Framing: The Behavioral Guidelines and Four Rs in the Family   105
Interior Design: Proactive Planning   109
The Seductiveness of Interference   115
Josie and Melanie: Maximum Support, Minimum Interference   119
WED: A Question and Answer Session with Joe   123
Conclusion   131

Appendix: Duncan's Translation of Joe's Conceptual Diagram   133
The Diagram: Philosophy   135
The Diagram: Methodology   141

Selected Supporting Material   147

Index   149

Respect
I stop to see the other as me.

Dignity
I reflect balance.

Responsibility
I care for my influence on all things.

Compassion
I share joy and pain.

Perseverance
I commit to life.

ABOUT THIS BOOK

We've learned a lot about treating kids and their families over the years, both in our individual work prior to meeting each other and in our work together since opening Direction Behavioral Health Associates back in 2008. In this book we will share our experience and knowledge with parents concerned about their children's emotional health and behavior. The mental health system in the United States is fragmented, underfunded, and underdeveloped. And, to put it bluntly, it's hard to find good help these days.

When faced with concerns about their child, parents often don't know where to begin. They present to us with a whole array of questions. Some examples include:

- *Is there really a problem, or is this normal behavior at this age?*
- *Does my child need to see a therapist?*
- *Does my child need to see a psychiatrist? Does he need medication?*
- *Does my child need to be hospitalized?*
- *My spouse and I are on totally different pages as to how to deal with this problem—what can we do about that?*
- *Am I being too hard on my child? Too easy?*
- *Our child won't go to school—how do we handle that?*
- *Our child won't talk to us / her therapist / her psychiatrist. Now what?*
- *Different doctors keep giving our child different diagnoses. What's the deal here?*

And on and on and on.

In this book, it is our aim to help parents find answers to these questions and others like them. We hope to arm parents with the information they need to tackle the wide variety of challenges they may face in child-rearing, whether or not they ultimately decide to seek help from professionals. Along the way, we will dispel a myriad of myths related to mental health treatment—myths often unrecognized and perpetuated by practitioners themselves.

The scope of this book is intended to be broad. It is written for parents who are struggling with their children's use of social media, refusal to empty the dishwasher, or resistance to attending school. It is written for parents of children who talk of suicide, sneak out at night, or use drugs. It is written for parents of children who have bipolar disorder, autistic spectrum disorder, or schizophrenia. It's written for parents who feel like they can't tell which way is "up" anymore.

This book is divided into three sections. The first provides an introduction to the authors and our program at Direction, which will be useful for illustrative purposes throughout the book. We will take a look at the different types of imbalances that can cause problems for young people and can continue into adulthood. The second section offers an introduction to psychiatry and how we deal with so-called biological imbalances, like depression and bipolar disorder. The third offers an introduction to Wholeistic Education, our treatment approach at Direction for addressing "developmental imbalances." It provides both a lens through which we can understand the principles of good parenting and therapy, and also a practical model that can be implemented in any family, clinical, or other group setting.

You'll see scattered throughout some of the favorite sayings of Duncan's father, Dave Gill, MD, and his grandfather, Jock Gill, MD, both veteran psychiatrists themselves. Let's just say psychiatry runs in the Gill family.

You will also find repeated references to what we consider to be "good treatment," "good therapy," and "good parenting." Ultimately, however, "good" caregiving of any sort is defined by its success in raising children to be healthy adults. If your approach to parenting or your provider's approach to treatment differs wildly from what we advocate in this book, and if it is producing good results, by all means continue doing what you are doing. We believe in the "don't fix it if it ain't broke" axiom.

On the other hand, if what you are currently doing just isn't working, we hope this book offers you a fresh take and further insight.

A BRIEF INTRODUCTION
TO THE AUTHORS

February 27, 2008: Opening Night

On a winter's evening in 2008, Duncan, Joe, and Bob (the group's original third partner, sadly now deceased) met at Direction's new site for hurried last-minute preparations for the program's first clients, due to arrive the next day. On that exciting, anxiety-filled night, with more to do than time in which to do it, a serious blizzard added to the drama. The wind howled, and it seemed as if the storm was determined to drill through the crumbling mortar in the bricks of that old mill building that was to be their new home.

On that momentous evening, with a certain touch of foreboding in the air, each partner arrived with an undisclosed priority. Bob was working on his office. Joe was continuing to toil out back in the group room, which for the past couple weeks had become his IKEA purgatory. Duncan was making repeated trips to and from his car, bringing in armfuls of supplies into the office.

At one point, Joe realized he needed another Allen wrench and walked out into the blizzard toward his car.

Trudging through the driving snow, he saw Duncan removing what appeared to be large rolls of clear plastic and a large can of red exterior spray paint from his trunk.

"Whatcha gonna to do with that?" Joe asked.

"I can't stand the peeling paint on the front door—it looks ratty. Totally unprofessional." Duncan replied with a scowl.

"Yeah…you trying to paint it now…tonight?"

"Yup."

Joe's title of Program Director, and his unusually keen, slightly obsessive interest in aesthetics, naturally charged him with leadership responsibilities in terms of the physical space. He knew he was testing the support and patience of his new partners in discharging his duties (as he perceived them). So far, he had rejected three other potential sites they had visited, without being able to say exactly why ("They just didn't feel right"). Having settled on the old mill building, he painstakingly undertook the creation of an environment with what he considered to be a "clubhouse" feel, from carefully designing where all interior walls should go to prioritize natural light, to selecting all the right furniture, to handpicking and framing only classical art prints.

Joe found himself on the one hand pleasantly surprised that Duncan, a psychiatrist, was showing real interest in the image and feel of the place, but on the other a bit unnerved by Duncan's sudden laser focus on the door. After a moment's reflection, Joe put it out of his mind and returned to assembling furniture out back. He removed his shoes (completely unnecessarily), lest he mar the just-installed oak-laminate flooring—really, just the least expensive, most durable flooring the trio could afford.

An hour or so later, Joe noticed his socks were turning red.

It didn't take him long to realize what had happened. With the unwanted assistance of the nearly hurricane-force wind, Duncan's mission to secure the presentability of the site with a fresh coat of red paint—with the door wide open—became an unwitting repainting of the entire interior of Direction's new space.

Racing up front, without a word, Joe began frantically ripping at plastic as he kicked the door shut. Confused by Joe's uncharacteristic alarm and reactivity, Duncan simply took a step back, as if taking shelter, calmly analyzing the situation from a safe distance. Joe dramatically pointed to his socks, silently miming a "critical communique" that he was sure Duncan understand.

Realizing what he had done, Duncan uttered nothing more than a bemused, "Oh, no."

For a brief but very real moment, Duncan and Joe stared at each other. Joe found himself confronted with a seemingly significant, hitherto unrecognized aspect of Duncan's personality. For his part, Duncan found himself abashed that he had allowed his impulsive, shoot-from-the-hip alter ego to reveal itself at a very unfortunate time. Both became suddenly very aware of their differences in temperament, personality, background, education, and clinical experience. How could this partnership possibly work? For a few seconds, the very fate of the enterprise appeared to hang in the balance.

Then the moment passed, and the two began the arduous process of cleaning the floors and walls, working together.

WHO ARE THESE GUYS, ANYWAY?

"This kid doesn't need meds; he just needs to smarten up."

—Joe Walsh, LCMHC

Joe spoke the above words in Duncan's outpatient office about twelve years ago, as they discussed one of the wayward teenagers from a residential program where Joe worked as a therapist.

At the time, it was a good illustration of each of their very different starting points: Duncan, a psychiatrist trying to get a child's explosive temper under control with medication; and Joe, an informal behaviorist, who distrusted medication and wouldn't even take Tylenol for a fever.

The two had only recently met, and their differences, at least on a superficial level, were striking. Duncan was a fourth-generation Harvard grad, third-generation psychiatrist, and a conventional-looking, conventional-sounding, pragmatic "man of science." Joe, on the other hand, earned his degree in street smarts, growing up as an adoptee into a Sicilian family living on the wrong side of the tracks. He was idealistic and artistic, drawn to Eastern philosophy, and suspicious of Western medicine.

It's fair to say that despite liking and respecting each other, Joe and Duncan entered their professional relationship with some mutual distrust. Joe's experience with psychiatrists in the past had not inspired a whole lot of faith in the field. And his seeming fixation on a system he created—entitled (misspelled?) "Wholeistic Education"—honestly left Duncan scratching his head and slightly concerned.

Nevertheless, the two found out they had much in common. In addition to a shared love of guitars and sports, the two both had clinical experience dealing with a wide spectrum of mental and behavioral problems. Duncan had worked for years in a variety of clinical settings, including inpatient units, outpatient clinics, and group homes. He had treated five-year-olds with anxiety about school, sixty-five-year-old incarcerated patients with schizophrenia, and pretty much everything in between. Joe, for his part, had worked for years in a supervisory position at Nashua Children's Home, a local residential program for troubled children with some of the most traumatic pasts imaginable. It was there that he implemented across the residence the aforementioned program called Wholeistic Education for the first time, resulting in a reduction in physical restraints by 96 percent in the first year.

Most importantly, Duncan and Joe shared a passion for what they did, a frustration with traditional "treatment as usual," and a conviction that they could do better.

So, ignoring the warnings of others about the risks of opening their own mental health business, they quit their jobs and created Direction Behavioral Health Associates. Direction would offer the area's only intensive outpatient program (IOP) for adolescents struggling with mental health issues. Later, they added a partial hospitalization program (PHP) to offer a slightly higher level of care as well.

Direction's IOP and PHP consist of a bundle of services: psychiatric evaluation, group therapy, medication management when appropriate, and work with families. Children come daily for either three hours (for the IOP) or six hours (for the PHP). The program is paid for by insurance and typically lasts a few weeks.

Direction serves young people between the ages of twelve and eighteen who have been referred by emergency rooms, schools, inpatient units, outpatient providers, and elsewhere. They present with problems ranging from conflict with their families, history of trauma, serious drug and alcohol abuse, school-based anxiety, autistic spectrum disorder, bipolar disorder, schizophrenia, and virtually all other mental health and behavioral issues.

Twelve years and three thousand clients later, the program has proven itself to be a major success in serving area youth and their families. Along the way, the mutual suspicion that Joe and Duncan shared for each other's methods evaporated, as they realized that their two different approaches were not at odds at all, but rather entirely complimentary.

About a year ago, Duncan approached Joe. "Maybe we should write a book about this whole thing?"

"Yeah," replied Joe. "Parents have been telling me for twenty years that they really could use it!"

PART 1

GOALS, IMBALANCES, AND HOW WE CAN HELP

How We Define Success

"I'm not in the 'feel better' business, I'm in the 'function better' business."

—Dave Gill, MD

Many parents ask what results they can expect by enrolling their kids in our program. This is a perfectly reasonable question for which we don't have an easy answer. Some kids progress by leaps and bounds, and the results are obvious to them, their parents, and us. Other times, progress is less obvious—or sometimes not apparent at all (though for these kids we hope that we are able to "plant seeds" that will germinate in time). What we *are* confident of is that each child will have a rich, educational experience. After the child's first day here, he or she will know that strangers can join with others in a positive, caring group. For many young people who didn't know it when they arrived, even this realization can be revolutionary.

"Progress," of course, also depends on how you define it. Is it a child's learning to control his temper? Returning to school? Simply "feeling better?" Different parents may have different goals for their children and different ways of defining treatment "success." Sometimes parents have unreasonable goals for their children or selfish goals that may not be in the interest of the children themselves. For example, some parents may just want their children to be "easier to control" for the sake of making their own jobs simpler.

We, on the other hand, have a single, universal treatment goal for all our clients, and it may not be what you think. Most people assume our goal is to help children "feel better." It's not.

It's not our job to make children "happy." We're not even sure what "happiness" is—it's a hard term to define. The quickest way to "feel better" or "happy" is to head down to the street corner. There, one can be guaranteed to find something that tweaks the brain chemistry into a sense of relaxation, euphoria, blissful numbness, or whatever other mental state one is seeking. It's the quickest way to make physical and mental pain disappear—at least for a while. The problem is that it is a short-term fix, and most people would agree that the long-term negative impact caused by making this solution a habit outweighs any short-term gains.

Which brings us to our true goal: our job is to help our clients *function* better.

Unlike "feeling better," "functioning better" is a tangible, sustainable goal. It does not guarantee "feeling better," but people who function better are more likely to have richer, more content lives. Functioning better means healthier relationships, better ability to perform one's job, and increased capacity to respond to stressful situations. It means a greater likelihood to identify and seize life's opportunities and handle life's setbacks.

In short, feeling better ("happiness?") is often, but not always, a side effect of functioning better.

This brings up an important point: *functioning better sometimes makes people feel worse, at least in the short term.*

Consider an eighteen-year-old girl who wants to quit drinking because it is interfering with school and her relationship with her parents. Our goal is to help her eliminate a bad habit that is impairing her functioning. (As you will see, much of our work has to do with replacing bad habits with good ones.) What's step one here? She needs to quit drinking. This is guaranteed to make her feel worse in the short term. Over time, however, as she learns to replace her bad habit with healthier ones, she will function better and hopefully feel better eventually as well.

Or consider an anxious twelve-year-old boy who wants to play baseball but has a habit of avoiding stressful situations. Step one: Try out for the team. This is guaranteed (at least during tryouts) to make him feel more anxious. The idea, of course, is that the experience—regardless of whether or not he makes the team—will be good practice at pushing through his anxiety, an ability that will serve him well later in life.

What about medication, though? Many people assume that part of our goal is to make children "feel better" through pharmacology (i.e., by prescribing "happy pills").

Nope. If the medication we prescribe makes a client feel better, that's great, but it's not the point. We consider it a bonus. In some cases, clients may function better but feel worse due to the use of medication.

Consider a fifteen-year-old girl with a clinical depression who shows a good response to an antidepressant and initially feels much better. However, due to her depressive symptoms, over the years, she has developed an attachment to being "unwell," having her parents and friends dote on her, and avoiding responsibility. Suddenly, she's functioning better, able to engage, and has more motivation, but she is faced with the prospect of giving up the role she's assumed as an "unwell" child. Because of deeply entrenched habits, this is going to be a real challenge for her—one that may well be quite difficult to tackle from an emotional standpoint.

Or consider the seventeen-year-old bipolar boy who is in the midst of a manic episode, staying up for four days straight, working on an invention that he is convinced is going to make him billions of dollars. He feels great—we mean really, really great. But he stopped going to school, got fired from his job, and sabotaged his relationships with his parents and girlfriend. Through the use of medication, we get the mania under control, and now his mood is "normal." He's furious because "normal" feels so much worse than the euphoria he was experiencing. He is feeling worse but functioning better.

Okay, so the goal of good mental health treatment is to help people function better. What's the endpoint here? How do we really define success?

We've achieved success when our clients are functioning well enough that they don't need us anymore. Save the occasional medication refill for someone like the bipolar seventeen-year-old, our services are no longer required. Our work is done. Next patient.

The Goal of Good Parenting

The goal of good parenting is pretty much the same as that of good mental health treatment: teaching children to function better.

To be sure, there are some key differences between being a parent and being a therapist. Therapists are (modestly) better paid and can go home at the end of the day. Parents, on the other hand, have ethical and legal obligations to their children that therapists simply do not. And, of course, the emotional ties between parents and their children are vastly different from those of a therapist and client.

As parents, we have eighteen years (give or take) to help our children learn to function well enough to become mature, independent members of society. As adults, they need to be able to function without us.

Put another way:

"The ultimate goal of the good parent should be to become obsolete."
(Dave Gill, MD)

Consider that statement for a moment. We need to teach our children to not need us anymore. This evolutionarily makes sense: our children usually outlive us and therefore need to be able to survive without us.

Human nature being what it is, the idea of becoming "obsolete" is a bitter pill for many parents (and therapists) to swallow. It's nice feeling wanted, feeling needed, feeling relevant. Many parents (and therapists) selfishly allow these wants to interfere with the child's (or client's) development. This can be a big problem.

As parents, we need to remain attuned to this trap. Everything we do should be done in the service of promoting our child's independence. Our goal should be to put ourselves out of business.

As noted before, however, as parents we also have ethical obligations, such as keeping our children safe. While allowing a child to play outside in a thunderstorm could be viewed as encouraging independence, it's not something we should do—this is probably a time in which we should intervene! Being a parent means striking a difficult balance between allowing the greatest degree of freedom for a child while simultaneously safeguarding his or her chances of surviving into adulthood.

Here's another way of looking at this:

"Good parenting = maximum support, minimum interference."
(Jock Gill, MD)

Unfortunately, there seems to be an increasing trend in American society to err on the side of "protecting" children rather than promoting independence. Fears about child abduction lead to fewer children playing outside, fears about a "C" on a report card lead to parent-generated homework schedules, fears about a child's not eating enough lead to regimented, managed meals. People from earlier generations call it "helicopter parenting," which is basically a form of interference. It is a real problem in today's society that inhibits children's natural exploration, growth, and learning through trial and error.

Moreover, a "micromanagement" approach to child-rearing is often encouraged by well-meaning but misguided therapists. Usually, it results in one of two problems. The first is active rebellion by children against what they (correctly) perceive to be efforts to control them. The second is their conformance to excessive parental demands, and their consequent persistent anxiety about the dangerousness of the world. After all, why would parents be so protective if the world wasn't a very dangerous place?

The bottom line is that good parenting requires never losing sight of the primary goal: that our children become independent and no longer need us. Consider it to be a bonus if they ultimately end up with enough positive feelings toward us that they grace us with their presence at Thanksgiving dinner every now and then.

IMBALANCES:
OBSTACLES TO GOOD FUNCTIONING

"Little by little we human beings are confronted with situations that give us more and more clues that we are not perfect."

—Fred Rogers

When children come to Direction, our first order of business is figuring out what the problem is. What exactly is impairing their functioning?

For the sake of argument, let's assume here that there *is* truly a problem with a child, and it's not a question of the parents having unrealistic expectations or goals that are counter to the child's best interest.

Roughly speaking, we can divide the problems we see into two categories:

- **Biological imbalances**
  More colloquially referred to as "chemical imbalances," these represent pathological disturbances in the brain that lead to clinical depression, anxiety disorders, bipolar disorder, and other psychiatric conditions.

- **Developmental imbalances**
  These may be also referred to as "behavioral" or "psychological" problems. When it comes to children, we prefer the term "developmental imbalances" because these problems are invariably intertwined with childhood development through various stages of growth. They include basically everything not considered "biological," including growing pains, immaturity, psychological hang-ups, maladaptive responses to stress, bad habits, and so forth.

It should be noted that the division we make between these two categories is purely artificial. Ultimately, everything can be considered "biological" in that even developmental problems originate in the brain, which is essentially a tangle of neurons. If we were clever enough, we could map out the neural networks of the brain and see the incredibly complex patterns that result in immaturity, poor relationship skills, and poor ways of coping with stress. If we were even more clever, we could surgically go in and rewire these neurons so that children had perfect relationship skills, handled stress flawlessly, and cleared their dinner plates without fail. All the stuff of a good dystopian novel. For better or for worse, however, we won't be doing that surgery anytime in the foreseeable future.

So if the distinction between these two types of imbalances is arbitrary, why even make it at all? Because, absent the aforementioned sci-fi surgery, making this distinction is the best way to determine what type of intervention will work for a given problem.

Trying to treat a biological imbalance with "talk therapy" will be of limited or no value. No talk therapy in the world is going to make a person with schizophrenia stop hearing voices or level out a bipolar patient's wild mood swings. Proper medication use, on the other hand, will help in both these cases.

Conversely, trying to treat a developmental imbalance with medication won't work. Giving a tantruming teenager Prozac is useless. As is giving lithium to a child who just experienced a breakup with her boyfriend and is suffering from plain-old heartache. Proper parenting and/or good therapy, on the other hand, may well help in both these cases.

The problem is that figuring out which imbalances are biological and which are developmental can be really tricky. Moreover, often both types of problems are at play simultaneously. A sixteen-year-old boy may have an explosive temper because he both inherited the genetics for mood instability (a biological imbalance) and acquired the bad habit of using his temper to get what he wants (a developmental imbalance).

And here's an important point:

Many of the children we see who have failed to make progress in the past in treatment have failed to do so because treatment providers have misclassified the nature of the children's imbalances.

We see this all the time: children who come in on eight different medications whose main problem, at the root, is developmental. Or children who come in who have been in and out of therapy for years with no progress to show because they have biological conditions that have gone untreated.

Worse yet:

Treatment providers who make this mistake often compound it by refusing to change their minds when presented with evidence that their initial assessment was wrong.

This is a problem of hubris. (And we'll discuss this further in the next section of the book.) For now, let's take a look at some further distinctions between biological and developmental imbalances.

Features of Biological Imbalances

In terms of the "nature-nurture" distinction, biological imbalances can be considered "nature" and are very often genetic. They are usually diagnosed and treated by psychiatrists and psychiatric nurse practitioners, and treated with medication.

Examples of biological imbalances include clinical depression, bipolar disorder, ADHD, schizophrenia, and autism. In this category, we also include functionally impairing psychiatric symptoms (like mood instability or excessive anxiety), even if not obviously part of a distinct "disorder."

Psychiatry is one of two medical fields devoted to the study of the brain, with the other being neurology. (It should be mentioned that both anesthesiology and pain management spend a lot of time tinkering between the ears as well.)

What's the difference between psychiatry and neurology? A simple way to conceptualize their relationship is that psychiatry can be viewed as poorly understood neurology. Both Alzheimer's disease and schizophrenia are undeniably medical problems. It's just that Alzheimer's is better understood and can be definitively diagnosed (though it requires brain dissection after death). Strokes show up on MRI. Seizures show up on EEG. Psychiatrists have very little to go on in terms of "objective tests," though our understanding of the different ways chemistry gets out of whack in different disorders is continuously improving, and our treatments are generally very effective when used properly.

In fact, psychiatry can be viewed as a shrinking field: many illnesses that were once considered "psychiatric" (e.g., neurosyphilis) have been taken over by neurologists once doctors gained a better understanding of what exactly was going wrong at the cellular level.

The three main hallmarks of biological imbalances are as follows:

- They often appear to be driven internally and have a life of their own, largely independent of what is going on in the environment.
- Because they are often genetic, we usually see a family history of similar psychiatric disorders or substance abuse in the family. They also more frequently turn up in children who have endured injury to or abnormal development of the brain before, during, or after birth.
- They tend to show a positive response to medication.

Features of Developmental Imbalances

We can view developmental imbalances as being on the "nurture" side of the equation, because they are usually products of experiences during growth and development, family dynamics, and parenting over the years.

Developmental imbalances include psychological problems (e.g., issues arising from family relationships during childhood), personality problems (e.g., selfishness, blaming others for one's problems), and bad habits (allowing one's anxiety to keep one from pursuing relationships, taking one's anger out on others, poor relationship skills).

The "medical model" is much less useful for conceptualizing developmental imbalances than biological ones, and we turn to other models of understanding, such as behavioral psychology, psychodynamic theory, and a host of others.

Here are a few features of developmental imbalances:

- They often appear to have a direct correlation with external circumstances, particularly interpersonal relationships.
- They show little response to medication but can show a good response to parenting, therapy, behavioral interventions, or even just tincture of time (i.e., growing up).
- There is a very strong relationship between parenting and developmental imbalances. That is to say, they can be exacerbated (or even created) by certain parenting approaches. Alternately, they can be mitigated (or even extinguished) through others.

Distinguishing Biological Imbalances from Developmental Imbalances

Every child struggles to some degree with developmental imbalances—some more so than others. The percentage of children who have a significant biological imbalance contributing to their problems is relatively low, but it's important to identify the ones who do. Competent mental health providers can usually tell the difference.

At Direction, we can usually tell the approximate mix of biological versus developmental imbalances contributing to a child's problem during the initial interview. This is primarily because we've done thousands of such interviews before. Sometimes it's not obvious at first what we are looking at, and it takes a while for us to sort it out. An advantage of running the type of program that we do is that we get to see children over the course of several weeks. Occasionally our initial assessment is flat wrong. If so, we change our assessment and modify the treatment plan accordingly. Staying humble in this profession is really, really important.

Responding to Imbalances: Where Should Parents Start?

"When you really want to sound like an arrogant doctor, you should add the word 'dammit' to the end of your sentence."

—Joe's advice to Duncan a few years ago

We've covered a few important concepts so far, including the goal of good parenting and good therapy (i.e., making ourselves obsolete), and the usefulness of distinguishing between biological and developmental imbalances.

Meanwhile, your fourteen-year-old son has been raising hell at home, and your twelve-year-old daughter has been refusing to go to school. Now what?

A reasonable approach would be to consider the following interventions, probably in the order given below:

1. Good parenting
2. Good therapy
3. Good psychiatric treatment

We feel compelled to qualify each of the above with the "good" prefix simply because it is an unfortunate fact that each intervention has an evil twin.

At Direction, we take advantage of all three interventions by offering parenting groups for parents, group therapy for the kids, and medication management.

The Role of Good Parenting

"Good parenting" is number one on our list for a reason. For most children, it will be sufficient to help guide them through the trials and tribulations of growing up without the need for professional help. For the children who *do* require outside intervention (whether therapy or medication), good parenting is still equally—and possibly more—important.

The best place to start as a parent is to prepare yourself for the possibility that your parenting approach is contributing to—or even the root cause of—your child's developmental imbalances.

This is a tough fact to face for many parents. It demands humility, open-mindedness, and willingness to accept the real possibility that you are making things worse, not better. (The good news is that if you are reading this book, you have a good chance of being one of those parents willing to look in the mirror.)

Some parents won't do it, period. This makes it much more difficult for us (or anyone else) to help their children.

Not only is good parenting often the single most important intervention available, but sometimes it is the *only* intervention available. This becomes the case if a child is unwilling to acknowledge a problem or participate in efforts to improve the problem. A child may refuse outside help altogether, whether it be therapy or psychiatric treatment, even if it might be of significant benefit. For parents of these children, the best option they have is to be rock solid in their resolve to parent in the manner most likely to promote positive development of their child while ensuring safety in the home.

The Role of Therapy

If efforts to parent in the most effective way possible are insufficient, you might consider enlisting professional help.

Parents usually begin by finding a therapist for their child. Individual therapy can be very helpful for some children, provided you find a good therapist. Unfortunately, this is often hard to do.

There are many different flavors of therapy. Some of them include:

- **Individual therapy**
  One-on-one therapy itself comes in many varieties, including insight-oriented therapy, cognitive behavioral therapy, and interpersonal psychotherapy.

- **Group therapy**
  Group therapy can be particularly useful for children for several reasons. One is that children really benefit from feeling they aren't alone in their struggles. Another is that children often listen to their peers better than they do adults. They feel they have enough adults telling them

what to do already. Wholeistic Education is used as our group therapy model at Direction.

- **Family therapy**
Family therapy can be very helpful for some children, because very often family dynamics and patterns are contributing to the problem.

Some kinds of therapy work better for some children than others. Perhaps more importantly, some *therapists* work better for some children than others. Some therapists are simply more skilled, relate better to children, and don't lose sight of that goal of good therapy: promoting the healthy and sustainable independence of their clients.

The Role of Psychiatric Treatment

For some kids for whom biological factors are more significant, enlisting the help of a good psychiatrist (or nurse practitioner) can be invaluable. Just like therapists, psychiatrists are in short supply, and the really skilled ones who can relate well to kids are even harder to find.

In general, whether you are seeking a therapist or psychiatrist, important qualities to look for include

- an understanding of and adherence to the principle of promoting independence, not dependence;
- an ability to form a positive connection with your child;
- open-mindedness, humility, and a willingness to admit being wrong; and
- a sense of humor, which sure is a bonus particularly with children.

These qualities are hard to find in a treatment provider. In our experience, it's becoming increasingly popular to "talk a good game" while still failing to deliver. More treatment "gurus" are saying the right things about promoting independence, and avoiding efforts to interfere or overcomplicate things. Nevertheless, it's one thing to say the right things and another to do the right things. Too many don't.

In any event, let's get back to the three areas of intervention: parenting, therapy, and psychiatry. We'll talk about each in turn in the remainder of the book, starting in reverse order with psychiatry, because it is the shorter, simpler section.

And because Duncan's the doctor, dammit.

PART 2

BIOLOGICAL IMBALANCES

THE STRAIGHT DOPE ON PSYCHIATRY

Psychiatry's focus is on biological imbalances that can impair people's functioning, in both children and adults alike. Psychiatry is the world of mood instability, depression, anxiety, and psychosis. In youth, we also can see the beginnings of more defined psychiatric conditions, such as bipolar disorder and schizophrenia. The staple treatment of biological imbalances is medication.

It is important to note here that most struggling children do *not* have biological imbalances significant enough to warrant medication. Most children's challenges are developmental in nature and all a part of the difficult process of growing up.

At a place like Direction, however, we see a disproportionate number of children who do have significant biological imbalances. The reason is that we see a skewed population—those children in the greatest need. It is critical to identify these children because they are at the highest risk. For some of them, medication is the single most important intervention we can make.

The purpose of this section of the book is to offer a down-to-earth, readable, and hopefully entertaining introduction to the fascinating and perplexing field of psychiatry, particularly as it relates to children and adolescents. We furthermore hope that after reading this section, parents who are pursuing psychiatric care for their children feel better informed and more confident walking into the doc's office for the first time.

SUSAN: THE CASE FOR MEDICATION

Susan was a young woman with very serious bipolar disorder—a condition that, once seen, is undeniable and unforgettable. She had been in our program many times over the years, usually after stopping her medication without consultation and suffering a recurrence of her bipolar symptoms. Her reasons for stopping medications varied: sometimes she ran out of medication, or her psychiatrist left the practice, or she was just looking to recapture that incredibly seductive manic feeling.

Her symptoms included mood swings from euphoria to severe anxiety to suicidal depression. She logged numerous very serious suicide attempts in the past, as well as inpatient hospitalizations. Her delusional thinking included believing that she could control the weather, that maggots were eating her brain, and that Duncan was trying to poison her. She once even called our emergency line—speaking with Duncan—because she knew her (presently) driving ninety-five miles per hour on the interstate, not caring if she lived or died, suggested something was wrong.

When on the medication that Duncan prescribed, she was a completely different person. Her delusions went away and she stopped being a constant risk to herself and others. She was able to work on developmental imbalances and able to begin thinking about the rest of her life.

Despite repeated early incidences of clandestine discontinuance of her medication, Susan invariably would show back up at Direction, whether in a manic, depressed, or psychotic state, and ask to begin treatment again. She generally quickly stabilized on medication and was able to return to the community.

WHERE PSYCHIATRY FITS IN

"You think this is a science? Kid, you got a hell of a lot to learn."

—Words spoken by an exasperated ophthalmologist to one of Duncan's
fellow medical students, who was questioning the ophthalmologist's
diagnosis because it didn't fit all the "textbook" criteria

Medicine: Art or Science?

The practice of medicine is an art. More specifically, the practice of medicine is art informed by science. In this age of "evidence-based medicine" and "best practices," a lot of other physicians may object to this view.

In all the excitement generated by our rapidly advancing measurement techniques, understanding of physiology and genetics, and fancier and fancier scans, it is small wonder that physicians have gotten a bit giddy about the science behind medicine. It becomes tempting to gravitate toward the idea that at some point we'll have it all figured out: medicine will become a hard science like mathematics or physics, and we'll be able to feed information into a computer, which will spit out an accurate diagnosis and generate the perfect treatment plan.

We strongly doubt this will happen in our lifetimes. It might never happen.

Physicians will always be faced with complicating factors, equivocal test results, unusual presentations of illness, treatments that are supposed to work in a given situation but don't, and uncertainty. The human body is simply too complex, our measurements too crude, and our treatments too inconsistent to reduce medicine to a hard science.

That doesn't stop well-meaning physicians and researchers from trying to design "best practices"—ideal algorithms to tackle any given medical condition—which have become all the rage in inpatient and outpatient settings, for better and for worse—for better because they can be reasonable starting points from which to work, and may present good treatment for the majority of simple cases of a specific condition; for worse because they encourage a sort of "cookbook medicine" that doesn't take into account potential variables in a given case. Many doctors agree that the concept of "best practices" encourages linear thinking and subtly or not-so-subtly discourages creative thought.

In fact, "best practice" drives some medical practitioners absolutely nuts because changing up treatment based on external variables is a "deviation" from "best practice" that requires defending their position to administrators.

A related buzzword in medicine today is "evidenced-based practice." We ourselves find this term irritating because it suggests that, prior to recent years, we all engaged in "fantasy-based practice." Evidence-based practice means diagnosis and treatment faithful to "the literature," which is a fancy way of saying the sum total of all published research papers.

Of course, this makes a certain degree of sense. Who can argue with the importance of using science (the literature) to inform the art of medicine? The problem is that the emphasis on "evidence-based practice" has diminished the accepted importance of a clinician's own practice experience. It has created an atmosphere in which relying on one's own clinical experience is discouraged and even viewed with disdain. After all, who is one physician to challenge the conclusions of academic experts who have pored over the literature and established "best practices" built upon "evidence-based medicine"?

Here's a question: With whom would you rather be caught in a foxhole as the bullets are whizzing overhead? The officer who just graduated from West Point at the top of his class or the veteran soldier who has survived several years of actual war?

Experience counts for a lot.

The rational solution, of course, is to take into account the scientific research and the lessons learned from one's own clinical experience, along with a healthy dose of creative thought. This is the art of medicine.

Psychiatry as a Medical Field

Psychiatrists go to four years of medical school, two of which involve clinical training in various fields, including surgery, internal medicine, pediatrics, and obstetrics and gynecology. We then spend an additional several years in residency, specializing in psychiatry. We have an "MD" after our names and can prescribe medication.

It is important to note that psychiatrists are particularly vulnerable to falling into the trap of viewing their own medical profession as a "science" instead of an "art." The reason for this? Psychiatrists tend to be insecure creatures, and some have a secret fear that they aren't "real doctors." By becoming obsessive about "evidence-based practice," "best practices," and "the literature," psychiatrists can alleviate this anxiety by feeling more "scientific."

Of course, psychiatry is arguably more art than any of the other medical fields, simply because we have less science to inform us.

And, here's the bottom line: if a psychiatrist cannot accept the limitations of his or her understanding of pathophysiology, our diagnostic system, and conclusions based on research, he or she is pretty well doomed from the start. Because in an effort to alleviate their own insecurity, such psychiatrists tend to sacrifice their humility. This is a dangerous thing for any doctor to do. These doctors believe they know more than they do, and won't change their opinions even in the face of mounting evidence to the contrary. They won't stray beyond the realm of algorithms endorsed by "the literature." They will see black and white, but no shades of gray. They will be tunnel-visioned, compulsive rule followers.

On the other hand, those psychiatrists who remain open-minded, humble, and capable of admitting "I have no idea" can help a lot of people.

Psychiatric Diagnosis

"A rose by any other name would smell as sweet."

—William Shakespeare

Our Sketchy Diagnostic System

Bring a child to see three separate psychiatrists, and it's not uncommon to end up with three different diagnoses. Why is this?

Psychiatry occupies the nebulous zone between "neurology" and "developmental problems." Because we don't understand the pathophysiology (abnormal cellular processes) of these conditions well, they become difficult to define. Moreover, psychiatric disorders tend to be "on a spectrum," meaning it's possible to have more severe or milder versions of depression, bipolar disorder, PTSD, and virtually all the other psychiatric conditions. Worse yet, symptoms of various conditions often overlap.

To qualify as a psychiatric diagnosis, one could reasonably expect the same criteria as any other medical diagnosis. Namely, we should expect:

- A similar cluster of symptoms
- A similar progression/course of these symptoms over time
- A similar response to the same treatment
- Ultimately, the same underlying pathophysiology. Because the pathophysiology isn't well understood, one would expect new research that comes in over time to be supportive of the validity of the diagnosis.

So how do psychiatrists come to define the different diagnoses? Essentially, by committee.

Basically, a group of psychiatrists sits and argues as to what the different diagnoses should be and what criteria should be used for each. They publish their opinion in the *Diagnostic and Statistical Manual* (DSM), which contains lists of all the diagnoses and what criteria define them. These criteria are checkboxes for each diagnosis. Check enough of the boxes, and you qualify for that diagnosis. Every few years, based on further reflection and research, they get together and revise the DSM—adding, subtracting, or modifying diagnostic criteria.

If this all sounds subjective and imprecise, that's because it is. But it's what we have. The issue is that many psychiatrists disagree on the best diagnostic criteria for a given diagnosis, or question whether or not certain diagnoses even can be considered valid.

So ultimately some psychiatrists will diagnose an individual with bipolar disorder while others view the same individual as having schizophrenia.

What about all that research going on? Can't it provide us with answers? It helps—somewhat. However, there are a number of factors that complicate research in the field of psychiatry:

- As we've seen, our diagnostic system is shaky to begin with.
- As we've also explored, objective measures for psychiatric conditions are far and few between. We are left to devise "rating scales" that tend to be very subjective.
- Ethical concerns make it difficult to conduct studies (particularly the gold-standard so-called double-blind placebo studies) on people with more severe symptoms. This holds doubly true for children and adolescents.
- The interpretation of studies is difficult.

All this is a cause of considerable frustration for treatment providers, caregivers, and patients alike. It's enough to make many throw their hands up in the air and declare the whole exercise pointless. It's enough to make many think of psychiatry itself as a nonmedical, wishy-washy field. This is an understandable reaction shared by many in the public, and even many other doctors.

The fact of the matter, however, is that, despite its limitations, psychiatry offers life-changing and sometimes life-saving interventions for many people.

A good psychiatrist, like any good scientist, understands the limits of his or her knowledge, and combines his or her academic expertise and clinical experience to arrive at a formulation of the presenting problem and a suitable treatment plan. Furthermore, he or she is humble enough to adjust this formulation and treatment plan based on any new information (e.g., responses to administered treatment) that becomes available.

The Importance of the Diagnostic Interview

What's the best technology available for psychiatric diagnosis? Language. Observation. A face-to-face interview.

There is no substitute for the clinical interview in psychiatry. It remains the gold standard in terms of establishing diagnoses. We are frequently asked by parents to have their child "tested" for conditions such as bipolar disorder, ADHD, whatever. We tell them the "test" is occurring as we speak—it's the interview. There are alternative formal, standardized "tests" (some of which are written or done on a computer) developed by psychiatrists, psychologists, and others, many of which have utility in certain circumstances. However, they generally play a supporting role in the diagnostic process. Diagnosis is established by talking with patients, observing them, and gathering collateral information.

There are no blood tests for bipolar disorder or depression, or any other psychiatric disorder for that matter. You can't diagnose schizophrenia on MRI.

This remains a fact despite advances in genetic testing, our identification of abnormal cellular processes at play through biochemical analysis, and certain types of brain scans.

Diagnosis is an art and will remain so for a long time to come.

Young People: A Diagnostic Mess

Many children present with psychiatric *symptoms* rather than well-defined *conditions*. They present with depressive symptoms, anxiety symptoms, and mood instability, but the symptoms obviously aren't part of a bigger constellation that define adult psychiatric conditions.

Part of this is because all psychiatric conditions are on a spectrum anyway—there can be different degrees of bipolar disorder, depression, OCD, and so forth. Rather than seeing textbook-defined "illnesses," we often see symptoms or symptom combinations of a greater or lesser degree.

What makes child and adolescent psychiatry different, however, is that many cardinal psychiatric conditions (e.g., bipolar disorder and schizophrenia) do not "crystallize" or "declare themselves" until a person's late teens or twenties. Nobody knows why—this is just the way it is.

Often, we will find symptom combinations that make us suspicious that a person is developing such and such a condition, but often it isn't clear. Sometimes symptoms just recede or go away entirely.

Child and adolescent psychiatry is tough because you are looking at children who might be developing a major adult psychiatric condition but have not done so yet. Moreover, we have to take into consideration the myriad of developmental imbalances common to youth. It's like taking a whole bunch of factors and putting them into a blender, and then asking someone to make sense of it all. These factors include typical growing pains, puberty, family conflict, personality development, struggles with peers, and separation/individuation dynamics, among others. All these developmental factors are present, in addition to biological contributions to the mix.

The good news for treatment is that it doesn't much matter whether or not someone has biological symptoms that are developing into a full-blown "adult" condition or not. A simple rule of thumb is that functionally impairing symptoms warrant the consideration of treatment.

A Quick Aside about Adult Psychiatric Conditions

It may be useful for the layperson to have some understanding of what mental illness can look like in the adult, after it has "declared itself," and is unobscured by developmental factors of childhood.

Adult mental illness offers a sobering reminder that, though psychiatry at times can be mistaken as a wishy-washy, touchy-feely field of medicine with little real application, there are absolutely concrete, debilitating illnesses out there that we can treat. Adult mental illness can look like a bipolar patient who speaks nonstop and has stayed up for literally seven nights in a row, insisting he has been sent by God to save the planet. It can look like the schizophrenic patient found wandering across the state without shoes in the snow, convinced that he is being followed by the FBI. It can look like the depressed patient who stops eating and drinking entirely because she thinks she has no right to live. It can present as misery, anger, anxiety, substance abuse, violence, and suicide.

These are very real medical conditions.

Psychiatrists and therapists who treat children and teens often don't see the biological extremes of mental illness, simply because they haven't shown up yet in our patients. But the above examples serve as important reminders as to where brain biology, when out of whack, can lead.

Psychiatric/Biological Symptoms

Of course, there are lots of reasons to feel depressed, anxious, or irritable. It's part of normal development. When factors such as family, peers, relationships, and school stress complicate this normal development, therapy can often be helpful.

In psychiatry, we are hunting for biological problems. These can be distinguished from developmental/psychological problems with experience. Here are a couple of important clues that a symptom may have a significant biological component:

- Depression, anxiety, mood instability out of proportion with environmental stressors
- Family history of depression, anxiety, mood instability, or substance abuse (Keep in mind that many people with substance abuse are self-medicating.)

Here's a list of the psychiatric symptoms we see most often in practice.

- **Depression**
  "I'm depressed" might be the single most common complaint. In addition to often being out of proportion to stressors, or part of the family history, biological depression usually is accompanied by so-called neuro-vegetative symptoms, which include insomnia, appetite disturbance, and the absence of the ability to find pleasure in anything. Severe depression can also lead to psychotic symptoms (see below).

  Depression generally responds well to antidepressants, though some children with a mood instability component can get more agitated or anxious on them, in which case a mood stabilizer may be necessary.

- **Mood instability**
  Although people often complain more about depression, we see mood instability just as often. Mood instability looks like emotional volatility, with ups and downs that seem to come and go on their own. It can also look like a mix of irritability, anger, and/or anxiety. Note that the "ups" don't have to be of manic proportions (e.g., feeling euphoric, on top of the world, talking fast, etc.) but certainly can. Mood instability also goes hand in hand with impulsivity, which often responds favorably to mood stabilizers.

Mood instability, taken to its limit, is called bipolar disorder. In addition to emotional volatility, bipolar disorder typically presents with a decreased need for sleep (unlike practically any other psychiatric or medical condition), racing thoughts, and sometimes psychotic symptoms.

In our experience, mood instability is more common in teens than adults, though for what reason we cannot say. It is also more dangerous in terms of suicide risk than straight depression, partially because people can go from feeling good or great to terrible in the blink of an eye.

Mood stabilizers can work wonders for these individuals.

- **Anxiety**

We see anxiety as generally being a secondary component of either depression or mood instability. That's the way it responds to medication, anyway: either antidepressant or mood stabilizer, depending on the clinical presentation. We don't typically prescribe "anxiolytic" medication, like benzodiazepines such as Valium or Ativan. These medications may have their place in certain limited circumstances for anxiety (or some medical conditions, such as alcohol withdrawal), but their addictiveness and depressant effects limit their usefulness for our purposes.

- **Psychosis**

Psychosis is impaired reality testing, manifesting as either hallucinations (sensory disturbances, usually auditory) or delusions (fixed false beliefs, such as believing the CIA is after you). It popularly is associated with schizophrenia, but also can be a symptom of bipolar disorder or even depression at times. It is important to remember that substances of abuse can also cause psychotic symptoms.

True psychosis usually heralds an adult-type psychiatric condition that requires treatment. At times, it can be difficult to distinguish "true psychosis" from childhood "creative thinking," imagination, PTSD-symptoms, outright making things up, or a mixture of these factors. This is where a psychiatrist's experience becomes important again.

Antipsychotics work great for hallucinations and delusions, and often can eliminate them completely.

- **Hyperactivity/inattentiveness**

We've saved this one for last because it's not something we often treat in our practice, simply because we usually have bigger fish to fry. Hyperactivity and inattentiveness rarely pose the same level of risk as other biological and developmental imbalances that we see.

In most cases, we conceptualize ADHD to be a product of societal and cultural demands that weren't there for the thousands of years back when we were hunter-gatherers. For most of human history, being a bit on the jumpy side and prone to rapid shifts of attention saved more people from tigers than the ability to sit still at a desk for hours at a time.

That being said, there do exist very effective treatments (such as stimulants) for children whose hyperactivity and inattentiveness are truly functionally impairing, and not simply the result of a mood, anxiety, or developmental problems.

PSYCHOPHARMACOLOGY 101

"Trial and error, trial and error."

—Dave Gill, MD

Where does this all leave us?

We simply do our best to identify biological symptoms that are functionally impairing and treat them. We don't know where these symptoms may be
leading. They might grow with time, they might stay the same, they might
disappear entirely. What matters is that they are putting a child at risk in the
present moment.

What kind of risk? Here are a few of the possibilities:

- Self-harm or suicide.
- Serious substance abuse. In our opinion, most serious substance abuse is
  the result of untreated mood or anxiety disorders.
- Isolation and impairment of social development.
- Disruption of relationships at home or school.

The staple of biological treatment in psychiatry is medication. There are
other forms (including electroconvulsive therapy, transcranial magnetic stimu-
lation, and other treatments under development), but medication is the current go-to treatment. Used correctly and in the right circumstances, the results
can be miraculous. They can be no less impressive than the response of infection to antibiotics. Counterintuitively, medicine is often most effective for the
most impairing conditions (e.g., bipolar disorder and schizophrenia).

Although we don't know exactly how the medication works, we have a
pretty good idea of the basics. Most medications appear to correct imbalances in brain chemistry—most commonly imbalances in "neurotransmitters,"
which are chemicals that serve as messengers between neurons. They employ

a variety of clever methods to boost certain neurotransmitters, lower others, block certain neurotransmitter receptors, and activate others. Many of the psychiatric medications were initially discovered by accident. Now scientists in the pharmaceutical industry have the ability to create and modify medications, tailoring their neurotransmitter effects. Over the past few decades, remarkable progress has been made in making these medications more effective, safer, and less likely to cause side effects.

Despite scientific advances, there is still a lot we don't understand. For example, we don't know who will respond to which treatment the best. Effective treatment boils down to identifying which people are likely to respond to medication and then implementing a judicious trial-and-error process. Here humility again plays a critical role: if a treatment isn't working, one must be ready and willing to shift gears. This might include changing to a medication within the same class, changing to a medication of a different class, or changing one's formulation of the problem entirely.

Choosing the class of medication to try is straightforward if one remembers the following rule of thumb: psychiatric medications should be selected on the basis of symptoms rather than diagnosis.

Put another way, we can effectively treat people without worrying a lot about "diagnosis." Keep this point in mind. We'll see in the section on Wholeistic Education that we can approach developmental imbalances the same way.

Here's a treatment algorithm for prescribing medication:

- Treat depressive symptoms with antidepressants.
- Treat mood instability with mood stabilizers.
- Treat psychotic symptoms with antipsychotics.
- Treat anxiety symptoms with either an antidepressant or mood stabilizer.

A combination of symptoms gets the corresponding combination of meds.

The process itself is simple: use symptom-specific medication in a trial-and-error approach. Of course, the devil is in the details. Simple doesn't necessarily mean easy.

The Decision to Try Medication with a Child or Adolescent

It can be difficult for parents to decide whether or not to have their child try medication. This is as it should be. We worry as much about parents who begin entirely gung ho about medication trials as those who are entirely resistant to the idea. Some parents are looking for a quick fix to complicated problems.

It all comes down to weighing the risks and benefits of a medication trial. Perhaps an easier way to look at it instead is weighing the relative risks of a child trying a medication versus *not* trying a medication.

Psychiatrists have a pretty good idea of the risks of various medications, as clinical trials of new medications are rigorous and most of the medications have been around for many years. A competent psychiatrist can explain potential side effects and risks of any given medication trial.

The risk of *not* trying medication is harder to gauge. Whatever biological element exists won't change for the moment, though over time it may improve or worsen. The trick is to assess the short-, medium-, and long-term risks of things continuing as they are. As described above, these risks can include self-harm, suicide, impulsivity, self-medication with substances, and impairment of social development.

The good news is that the short-term risks of most psychiatric medications are quite low. Most medications are "easy-on, easy-off," meaning they can be started and stopped easily. It often makes sense to consider a short trial on medication, as there is little to lose. If things don't improve dramatically, the trial can always be stopped.

A Few Common Myths about Psychiatric Medication

"Dunc has a pill for that."

—The team's running joke when faced
with a particularly difficult child

- *"Psychiatric medication is 'artificial' and therefore only 'artificially helps' one feel better."*
If one accepts that psychiatric conditions reflect real biological problems in the brain (which they undoubtedly do), treating psychiatric conditions should be no different from treating other medical conditions. Antihypertensives for high blood pressure or Tylenol for fevers can be viewed as similarly "artificial." Do they only "artificially help"? How about a cast for a broken leg?

    We chuckle when we hear a child object to taking medication because it isn't "natural," when the same child is smoking marijuana and drinking alcohol, or using any other number of drugs of abuse. We often hear that certain drugs, like marijuana, are "more natural." We suppose this is true. You can find arsenic in the wild too, but we wouldn't recommend eating the stuff.

- *"Psychiatric problems can be overcome simply through willpower."*
Grit and determination sure can help, and in some instances may be enough to get someone through. But no amount of grit or willpower is going to fix a profound depression, or bipolar disorder, or make voices from schizophrenia go away. It's like trying to use "willpower" to cure high blood pressure or diabetes.

That being said, taking care of oneself through diet and exercise and sleep habits are all important. In some cases, however, this simply isn't enough.

- *"Taking psychiatric medication is admitting defeat."*
See the above answer.

- *"It's a good idea to make a child take medication if he or she does not want to."*
This is usually a terrible idea. In fact, we won't prescribe anything without the child's go-ahead. In the next section of the book, we'll explore the importance of "avoiding adversarial dynamic" with a child.

   We will give our opinion to a child and parent as to whether or not we believe medication makes sense, but almost never push the issue if the child resists. Four out of five times, because of this approach, if a child truly needs medication, he or she will come to us a few days later to ask to discuss it further.

- *"It's a good idea to 'push through' feeling worse on a medication."*
This is often a bad idea, too. Sure, there may be early side effects (sleepiness, dizziness) that often go away relatively quickly after starting a medication trial. But any real sense from a kid that the medication is making him or her feel worse, particularly in terms of mood, is grounds for discontinuing the trial.

- *"You need to wait several weeks for medication to work."*
This is nonsense. We could write a whole chapter on this subject. Suffice it to say, after treating thousands of children and adults in outpatient, inpatient, and residential settings, we've seen hard evidence time and again that this is not the case. This myth, perpetuated by much of the psychiatric establishment, particularly infuriates some of our inpatient psychiatry colleagues, who see the rapid effects of medications and often have just a few days to get people well enough for discharge.

   Sure, effects can accumulate over weeks. But if we don't see some glimmer of improvement over the first few days, we're moving on to something else.

- *"Psychiatric medication is habit-forming."*
Virtually no psychiatric medication causes dependence, save a select few anxiolytics, which we rarely prescribe. Most can be stopped abruptly with little ill effect, other than its ceasing to work. We always recommend

tapering to be on the safe side, however, and some medications (particularly antidepressants) can cause unpleasant effects if discontinued abruptly.

- *"We won't be able to tell if the medication is working anyway."*
  If you or your child can't tell, it's probably not working (or working well, anyway). A positive response to treatment often looks like: "Wow, I wish we discovered this five years ago!"

- *"Psychiatric medication will fix my child's bad behavior."*
  Psychiatric medication does not fix behavior. It fixes problems with mood, anxiety, distortions in thinking, attention, and so forth. Behavior is much more complicated and often habit driven. To the degree that a child's mood, anxiety, reality testing, or attention is directly contributing to a child's behavior, his or her behavior might improve.

Speaking of behavior, it's time we leave the world of psychiatry and biological imbalances, and move on to explore developmental imbalances in children and what we can do about them.

PART 3

BEHAVIORAL IMBALANCES

An Introduction to Wholeistic Education

In the beginning of this book, we divided childhood imbalances into two categories: biological and developmental. The first section covered biological, or psychiatric, imbalances. It's time to move on and discuss developmental imbalances, which essentially include "everything else." These problems may also be referred to as "psychological" or "behavioral," and include immature responses to stress, underdeveloped social skills, boneheaded teenage behavior, and other bad habits and patterns that may be obstacles to good functioning. Is your kid refusing to go to school? Not taking out the garbage? Stealing, lying, or using drugs? Picking boyfriends that aren't good for her? This section is for you.

Good parenting maximizes the chances that kids overcome these imbalances and minimizes the amount of time it takes them to do so. On the other hand, "not-so-good parenting"—putting it nicely—will be less effective and take longer. It may perpetuate imbalances or even cause them. Unfortunately, much of what is conventionally considered to be good parenting is really not-so-good parenting in disguise.

We are going to take a look at the principles of good parenting that will maximize the chances that children will overcome their developmental balances and how to respond to behavior stemming from these imbalances.

As noted previously, the model we use here at Direction is Wholeistic Education (WED), a therapeutic approach developed by Joe embodying the principles of good parenting. It serves as the basis of group therapy and is also what we teach in parenting groups. Joe himself will tell you there is nothing exotic or new in WED; he did not "invent" any of the principles. Rather, he collated them and created a useful, practical way to organize, think about, and implement these principles in any group, including a family.

Even if you don't choose to implement WED at home, per se, WED offers us a useful framework in which to conceptualize the principles of good parenting.

On the other hand, if you want to reap its maximum benefits of WED, and would like to introduce WED at home, we are going to walk you through the process, step-by-step.

The structure of WED is simple. There are only five concepts that are absolutely required to understand it: the educational culture, the three educator objectives, the three educator challenges, the behavioral guidelines, and the four Rs.

Let's get started.

WHAT IS WHOLEISTIC EDUCATION?

"I sell pain."

—Joe Walsh, LCMHC,
only half-joking, to members of a parenting group

In a nutshell, Wholeistic Education (WED) is a comprehensive approach that is dedicated to achieving "optimal wellness," or the greatest possible sum of physical, emotional, and spiritual health. It has been developed by Joe over the past several decades, supported by his years of research into evolutionary psychology, philosophy, health, Eastern and Western thought, and a whole bunch of other disciplines. The simple reason it is called "Whole-istic" is that it is meant to address the "whole person" in his or her pursuit of optimal wellness. For example, it includes nutrition, exercise, and other physically based programs that are beyond the scope of this book.

For our purposes, we are interested in what WED has to say about healthy habits, relationships, and groups. Specifically, we want to see how WED can leverage the power of the group—your family—to facilitate your child's growth and help your child overcome his or her imbalances.

Prior to introducing it to Direction, Joe implemented WED at the residential treatment program at which he worked with very positive results. One of many benchmarks attesting to its success was the reduction of physical restraints at the program by 96 percent in one year.

Joe teaches WED to parents in our parenting group, where most parents find themselves introduced to a very different slant on parenting than they have heard before. For some, even just hearing this fresh perspective can be helpful. A large subset of these parents opts to integrate WED more fully into their own homes.

In addition to serving as the approach we teach in parenting groups, WED serves as the blueprint for Direction's group therapy program. In effect, we are teaching WED both to children (in the form of group therapy) and their parents (in parenting groups, family sessions, and mediation meetings). Everyone is learning the same thing.

How can WED serve as both a parenting system and a group therapy model? Because WED is all about creating healthy groups that foster individual growth. At home, the group is the family. At Direction, the group is "the group," which can be seen as serving as a surrogate family for the children.

Of course, WED is only one of many models that may be helpful to children and their families. We have chosen to use WED at Direction because it has several advantages over many alternative approaches:

- It is simple and easy to understand.
- Everyone, including parents and other group leaders, is held to the same standards.
- Because it is a behavioral approach, we are able to effectively help children even if we don't know the causes of their imbalances, biological or developmental.
- Because it is a behavioral approach, we are able to be effective leaders even if we don't fully appreciate or understand our own imbalances, biases, or flaws as parents.
- It is solution-based rather than problem-oriented.
- It has been proven to be effective in a wide range of environments over many years of use.

Like any treatment modality or parenting approach, WED also carries with it some disadvantages:

- While simple and easy to understand, it is *not* easy to implement, and requires dedication and patience.
- It is typically counterintuitive and requires a substantial shift in thinking for many parents.
- It is concerned with relationships and long-term family solutions, rather than specific solutions to immediate problems.

This last point deserves some further explanation.

It is common for parents to come to us seeking answers for their children's very specific undesirable behavior without looking at the bigger picture of their children's—or the family's—larger imbalances. We hear questions from parents about children's' concerning behavior all the time in parenting group.

"How do I get my child to stop playing video games 24/7?" "How do I get my child to go to school?" "How do I get my child to stop being so disrespectful?"

We frustrate parents because we offer no simple answers to the vast majority of these questions. That's because we believe there *are* no easy answers.

Here's how an exchange might go between Joe and a parent in parenting group:

> Parent: *"How do I make my kid go to school?"*
> Joe: *"Sorry, I don't have a simple answer for that type of question."*
> Parent: *"What am I doing here then? What am supposed to do?"*
> Joe: *"What we can offer is an approach, called Wholeistic Education."*
> Parent: *"OK, so Wholeistic Education is going to give me an approach for getting my kid to school?"*
> Joe: *"Well, not really. Wholeistic Education is going to give you an approach for creating a healthier family culture at home."*
> Parent: *"How's that going to help?"*
> Joe: *"Because then your family can solve this problem yourselves."*

WED is an approach that requires dedication and patience. This is what Joe means when he says he "sells pain" in parenting group. It takes the long view.

Joe expresses a special brand of contempt for certain "experts" in the field who espouse an approach that sacrifices long-term gains for short-term answers. He calls them "the unethical jerks preying on desperate parents by peddling easy, pain-free, and ineffective-at-best solutions to their specific problems." Ouch.

To summarize, WED is simple, but it's not easy to implement. It is abnormal, counterintuitive, and slow—sometimes glacially slow. Also, it's front-end-loaded like a mortgage. At first, you pay mostly interest and earn little equity. Joe warns parents not to tinker with WED. If you think it may be worth a shot, go all-in, all the way. If you don't, if you try to implement a partial version of WED at home, you are likely to accrue all the liability and miss all the benefits.

Basic Principles:
Habits and Groups

"I wish I could go to school here."

—Typical child after about two weeks in the program

Healthy and Unhealthy Habits

WED is what's known as a "behavioral approach" to addressing developmental imbalances. It concerns itself with modifying maladaptive behavior, not searching for the cause of the behavior or underlying motivation. The advantage of such an approach is that we don't need "full understanding" of a problem (which may be elusive and possibly unknowable) to go about fixing it.

Developmental imbalances very often are the result of maladaptive behavioral patterns. WED refers to them simply as "bad habits."

Contrary to the old saying "Practice makes perfect," practice actually just makes "permanent." Behavior that we repeatedly engage in, whether healthy or unhealthy, whether conscious or unconscious, becomes habit. "Bad habits" are the habits we establish that get in the way of our functioning. They are detrimental to emotional or physical health, or our ability to have healthy relationships.

Some obvious examples of bad habits might include:

- Eating junk food
- Leading a sedentary, inactive life
- Not caring for one's hygiene
- Smoking

51

"Bad" in this context has no moral connotation; it does not represent a condemnation of any sort. It just means these are the types of behavioral patterns that favor short-term rewards at the expense of long-term health.

Less obvious but equally detrimental bad habits exist in the social realm. They might include:

- Never admitting one is wrong
- Lashing out physically when angry
- Being passive-aggressive when emotionally hurt
- Avoiding situations that make one anxious

These habits essentially represent developmental immaturity. It should be noted that, as far as we can tell, we all have some bad habits left from childhood and remain immature in some respects. The good news is that our children are *supposed* to have bad habits—they are all immature by definition. They haven't had the chance to replace bad habits with good ones.

It's us, as parents, whose job it is to help children overcome their bad habits—the root of many developmental imbalances. WED can help by using the power of healthy groups to our advantage.

The Power of Groups

Overcoming bad habits is hard work. If it weren't, everybody, including our children, would be models of maturity. Establishing an exercise program, or quitting smoking, can feel really lousy for a while. Learning to manage our anger can be frustrating, being assertive can be daunting, and pushing through our social anxiety can be unsettling. Having the support of a group behind us as we work toward these changes can make a world of difference.

Groups, like habits, come in healthy and unhealthy varieties. Healthy groups promote the growth, development, and independence of their members. Unhealthy groups inhibit this growth and development and/or foster dependence upon them. Some groups are unhealthy because they are selfish and simply don't have the individual's best interests at heart. Others do have the individual's best interest at heart, but are ineffectual or counterproductive in their efforts to help.

What does a healthy group look like? Here are some characteristics:

- It has the best interest of the individual truly at heart.
- It is supportive of the individual's efforts to change his or her habits and behavior ("maximum support").
- At the same time, it is *not* supportive of an individual's existing bad habits. It does not "let them slide."
- It is as unobtrusive as possible in the individual's own exploration and creativity. It values and supports autonomy and independence ("minimum interference").
- At the same time, it demands commitment to a basic code of conduct that takes into consideration the needs of other individuals in the group.
- It is voluntary. That is to say, people are free to join the group if they are willing to commit to the group's code of conduct. They are not permitted to be part of the group if they are not committed. The voluntary nature of the group fosters and affirms an environment that supports autonomy and independence. (The special situation of obligations to children in families will be discussed in the next chapter.)

A group that meets the above criteria has a "healthy culture" (or "educational culture" in WED speak). In the group, there is a positive, collaborative spirit. Folks are on the same team, they help each other out, they care for each other. When conflict arises (as it inevitably does in any group), it is addressed and worked out.

In reviewing the above criteria, you'll note that "being supportive"—while a critical aspect of a healthy group—is only part of the equation. Caring for each other also means bringing attention to things (such as bad habits) that are getting in each other's way. This may mean bringing up difficult subjects, telling others things they don't want to hear, and potentially stimulating conflict. It means not enabling or supporting others' bad habits, either through action or failure to act.

You can see the power of a healthy culture in action at Direction. Children and their parents alike are amazed that such a disparate group of teenagers (boys and girls, ages ranging from thirteen to twenty, all walks of life, all sorts of problems) not only get along but actively help each other out and work through solutions together. They let their guard down in ways they have never done elsewhere. Because they feel supported by one another and the group at large, they accept being challenged by others and gently pressured by the group regarding their own maladaptive habits.

You kind of have to see it to believe it. This is the type of culture we are trying to establish in our families. As far-fetched as it may seem to some parents, in the vast majority of families, this culture can be achieved, no matter what the hostility meter reads at the present time.

MIKE:
THE MAGIC OF A HEALTHY CULTURE

North of 6-feet-tall, way north of 250 pounds, energetic and giddy with anxiety, Mike came to Direction after having struggled with significant autistic traits for years—namely the inability to "read" others or have confidence in his understanding of other people's subjective experiences. Almost mute with fear, after struggling through the initial intake interview (mercifully truncated), Mike marched directly to the most isolated spot in a corner in the back of our office. He remained there for the remainder of the day, the next day, and every day for the rest of the week.

Most providers and caregivers would have correctly recognized that much of the Mike's sadness was due to his lack of personal contact and meaningful relationships. However, many would have made the mistake of trying to impose their and other relationships upon him—causing him to be more afraid and averse. Direction was going to take the opposite tack and simply follow Mike's lead. (The interested reader might refer to WED's core value "Following" in the appendix.)

Somewhere near the end of the second week, staff noticed that though Mike's voice was still unknown to most in the group, the group's own voices held some evidently irresistible attraction for him. Going unnoticed at first, each day Mike thawed in the warmth of Direction's culture, and slowly, almost imperceptibly, he was joining the group. By the end of the third week, new members couldn't distinguish Mike from the other, fully integrated members of the group—that is, until he spoke.

In fact, Mike "found his voice" most unpredictably. It was during one of the most intense types of groups at Direction, as twenty attentive group members suffered through a young woman's graphic retelling of an abuse history. There was hardly a dry eye in the house, and one could hear a pin drop in what had become a cavernous space of whimpers.

Without warning, from across the room, Mike blurted out: "I found a dildo in a drawer last night."

The group—including the young woman—couldn't help but laugh. After a short interlude, she was able to recommence her story. At that moment, however, it was made crystal-clear that Mike had a lot more work to do. Fortunately—because he had been given the space he needed—he was now fully engaged in the group and was in a position to carry out that work.

How Wholeistic Education Creates Healthy Groups

"Showing is better than telling."

—Advice often given to aspiring writers

We've talked about what a healthy group looks like and how it can help individuals' growth and development. How do we go about creating such a group? Or, if we are in an existing group that isn't as healthy as it could be, how can we make it so?

It generally won't happen by itself. Somebody (or "somebodies") has to step up and lead the effort.

Group Leaders

When we talk about group leaders, we are usually referring to our group staff, at Direction, or you, the parent, at home. However, it is important to note that WED embraces the concept of "Wholeistic leadership," meaning anyone in the group—regardless of age—may be a group leader. A group leader in WED is defined as a person best embodying WED's principles (such as the behavioral guidelines) at a given point in time. In this way, leadership isn't arbitrary, nor is it exclusive to a certain person or set of persons.

(In WED, Joe prefers the term "educator" to "therapist" much as he prefers the term "education" to "therapy." He sees individual growth and development as a learning process like any other. You can find out more about his thinking on this matter in the appendix.)

The WED philosophy includes a number of sayings that describe the nature of healthy groups. They outline the principles that group leaders (be they parents or WED educators) rely on.

WED's Overarching Motto:
"Embrace All Feelings, Guide All Behaviors."

We need to acknowledge a fact of life: we can't control our feelings. Feelings are part of the human condition. Sometimes we feel happy, sometimes sad, sometimes angry, sometimes anxious. People tend to fall into the trap of thinking they "shouldn't" feel this way or that. This is nonsense. Feeling just are. As Joe says:

> *"Feelings are like the weather, unimaginably complex and not in our control. Most people get upset if it's raining on the day they've planned a picnic. But most people will not be paralyzed by upsetting emotion. After some (hopefully short) period of overwhelming feeling, most folks just change their plans or grab an umbrella! Humans seem to benefit from the knowledge that nature is busy with important work and so couldn't care less how they feel. Our overarching motto reflects the wisdom of that perspective and follows that dynamic sequence."*

Here are three common mistakes to avoid:

- **Blaming ourselves for our feelings.**
  As we've said, feelings just are.

- **Blaming someone else for his or her own feelings.**
  This is a double standard.

- **Dwelling unnecessarily on feelings.**
  This is a common mistake made by many people, including therapists. Many therapists in our opinion spend an undue amount of time discussing, validating, and probing a particular feeling, or searching for its "root." Finding "the root" might be helpful but is not always possible nor in many cases necessary. Energy is often better spent on seeking solutions.

Behavior, on the other hand, *can* be controlled. This brings us to three more common mistakes:

- **Believing feelings necessarily lead to behavior.**
  Feelings and behavior are entirely separate. Feeling a certain way can make us "want" to behave a certain way (e.g., punching our boss in the face because we are angry with him), but it doesn't "force" us to act in a certain way.

- **Believing we cannot control our behavior.**
  This is a corollary to the previous statement. In the vast majority of cases, a person *can* control his or her behavior. That's not to say it may not be really difficult, but it is rarely impossible. A common thought experiment Joe likes to present is the following: *"If someone offered you thirty million dollars if you didn't do 'x,' could you keep from doing it?"* If someone is being truthful, the answer is almost always "yes"!

- **Believing others cannot control their behavior.**
  This is letting others off the hook, absolving them of responsibility.

WED tells us to "Embrace all feelings" by acknowledging the real emotional experience of all individuals. It then tells us to "Guide all behaviors" and help the individual approach the problem at hand.

In a nutshell, the healthy group's attitude is *"Wow, John, it sounds like you had a really tough day. I'm sorry you are so down. Now what are you going to do about it? Can I help?"*

THE THREE EDUCATOR OBJECTIVES AND THREE EDUCATOR CHALLENGES

"Education is the ability to listen to almost anything without losing your temper or your self-confidence."

—Robert Frost

How do we become effective group leaders? WED proposes pursuing the three educator objectives listed below.

1. *"Model healthy relationships."*

The first rule of leadership is to lead by example. Talk is cheap. Show the group what healthy interactions look like and how conflict should be addressed. Be humble. Acknowledge mistakes made along the way. Apologize for them. At both Direction and at home, we want to be role models for our children.

Children can smell hypocrisy a mile away. A "do as I say, not as I do" attitude is going to make creating a healthy group much, much harder. If you have the habit of blowing up and losing control when angry, how can you expect your child to do any differently?

2. *"Provide clear reflection."*

Others can see us from angles that are hard for us to see. So, in some ways, we rely on others to know ourselves. To that end, as group leaders we need to "reflect," or mirror, our subjective experience in the group.

This is less important when things are proceeding swimmingly, the culture feels positive, and everyone is getting along. ("It's easy to be a sage on a mountain.") It is more important when things feel "off," when we feel tension in a relationship, when we are uncomfortable with a situation,

61

even if we can't put our finger on the exact cause. We need to acknowledge the elephant in the room and bring the group's attention to it.

At Direction it might be an uncomfortable silence suggesting a group member might have gotten her feelings hurt. At home it might be an unacknowledged adversarial feeling between you and your child—that the two of you don't seem to be on the same team.

The way we provide this reflection is critically important. Pronouncements of "facts" based on assumptions made with an aggressive tone are going to be met with defensiveness. Statements such as "There you go getting all bent out of shape again!" aren't going to help.

"Humble questions" (you'll see references to this term again and again) are the way to go. They are far less likely to provoke a negative response or inflame the situation. Humble questions might include "Sam—I'm worried I hurt your feelings. Am I right?" or "I feel like we aren't on the same team here, Bill. Do you feel the same way?"

Providing clear reflection through the use of humble questions can be difficult and often feels foreign to people. It is a skill that must be acquired through practice.

3. *"Encourage true focus."*
    Leaders keep the group on track. Regardless of whatever else is going on, maintaining the positive culture is essential. Leaders keep an eye on the group's overall health and look to address problems before they get out of hand.

These three educator objectives remind us what to do as group leaders. Now it's time to talk about what *not* to do as group leaders.

The Three Educator Challenges

WED's three educator challenges (listed below) are counterintuitive to many people. These are the ones that leave parents scratching their heads in parenting group. They go against the grain of conventional wisdom when it comes to dealing with children and teenagers. Many treatment providers pay only lip-service to them, or even offer advice directly contrary to them.

We believe them to be absolutely sound.

1. *"Give up control to gain authority."*

The group leader aims to respect the greatest amount of freedom possible ("minimum interference") of the individual while safeguarding a basic set of social expectations. Trying to "control" another individual, trying to "make" him or her do what we want, is a direct violation of this principle. There is no better way to create an adversarial dynamic (see below).

"Controlling" also runs counter to the principle of promoting independence and respecting autonomy. It does the opposite: it fosters dependence.

Attempting to control a child or teenager can look like helicopter parenting, parent-created schedules and regimens, nagging, or bullying. At its core, it demonstrates a lack of respect for autonomy. It also insulates the child from learning on his or her own through trial and error.

It should be said that "exerting control" has its place in times when emergent issues of health and safety dictate. You grab your toddler when he starts to run across the road. You don't want your child to learn about the dangers of playing in a thunderstorm the hard way. However, these times of real, significant danger are the exception rather than the rule. Flunking an English test is not an emergency.

"Authority," by contrast, is *voluntarily-granted influence* to a leader based on respect for and trust in his or her wisdom. Authority is earned through leading by example ("model healthy relationships"). You are unlikely to be granted this authority if you take a "do as I say, not as I do" approach.

2. *"Neither punish nor enable imbalanced behavior."*

What does a group leader do when faced with an individual's "bad behavior"? All too often, he or she commits one of two errors.

The first error is punishing the individual. Putting moral objections entirely aside, punishment is an ineffective way to deal with imbalanced behavior. It demeans the cooperative nature of the group, promotes an adversarial dynamic, and is an expression of control. While punishment may produce in one sense a "short-term relief" for the group from undesirable behavior of an individual, it does no service to the individual (or the group) in the longer term. It deprives him or her of the long-term educational benefit of learning from the natural consequences of his or her behavior.

Punishment comes in many forms: physical, verbal, public embarrassment, grounding, "time-outs" (usually for younger children), and so forth. We advocate against "punishment" of all forms in any group, including families.

The second error is enabling the individual. Enabling can be as damaging to a group member's development as punishment. In enabling, a leader is essentially looking the other way when faced with an individual's bad habits. Worse yet, he or she may actively support the habit. This response does nothing to promote the development of the individual and likely will retard it. The healthy group considers it to be its right, and more importantly its duty, to address maladaptive behaviors among its members.

Enabling is allowing an individual's bad habits to go unaddressed. It sometimes looks like excessive excuse-making for a child (e.g., "She can't help it—she is depressed"), giving in to a child's demands, or "walking on eggshells" at home to avoid provoking a child into threatening or violent behavior.

3. *"Avoid adversarial dynamic."*

The healthy group has a cooperative spirit. This is incompatible with members' viewing each other as adversaries or opponents. Adversarial dynamics are particularly common in relationships with teenagers, as they are in a developmental stage prone to combativeness anyway. Teenagers are also particularly adept at pushing buttons and drawing parents into a fight.

How do we extricate ourselves from the power struggles so common with our children? By not participating. You can't have a battle when only one side is fighting.

Note that adversarial dynamics aren't the same as conflict. Conflict is inevitable in any group from time to time, and can be either approached in a collaborative spirit or an adversarial spirit. The difference is that healthy groups approach conflict in the former manner.

What Are We Left With?

In dealing with the individual's bad behavior, WED tells us that the healthy group avoids some very common but misguided strategies: exerting control, punishing, enabling, and fighting back. What is a healthy group to do?

The healthy group respects the right of an individual not to commit to the group's social expectations, but at the same time does not support that individual's continued membership in the group. It respects the autonomy of the individual to choose whether or not he or she wants to be part of the group. This is consistent with the philosophy of supporting an individual's independence. As stated earlier, healthy groups are voluntary in nature.

Put another way:

The unhealthy group says, "You have demonstrated that you aren't committed to following our code, but that's no big deal," or it says, "You aren't following our code, but we can make you do so!"

The healthy group says, "You have demonstrated that you aren't committed to following our code. We respect your choice and your decision to leave the group."

For our purposes, it is critical that we view an individual's noncommitment to group social expectations—by word or by deed—to be his or her own decision not to belong to the group. This holds true no matter how loudly the individual may "verbally" insist otherwise. His or her actions have demonstrated a lack of commitment and therefore a choice not to belong to the group.

The healthy group does *not* view it the other way around (i.e. that the *group* is somehow making a decision for the individual). The group isn't "kicking out" the individual. The individual has *chosen* not to be part of the group.

Why is this distinction important? Because the healthy group is about respect for autonomy (e.g., the freedom of the individual to choose to leave the group). The unhealthy group is about imposing control on others (e.g., "kicking out" a member of the group). There is a big philosophical difference here that will be important to keep in mind as we look more closely into WED.

At this point you may be thinking that this may be all well and good for a group such as a soccer team or the Boy Scouts, but how can a child's place in a family be considered "voluntary" at all? It does present a conundrum, and this is why parents resort to the typical methods of dealing with "bad behavior" at home: exerting control, punishing, enabling, and fighting back.

WED proposes a solution to this problem, called *restriction*, that we will cover in a later chapter, in which we still can respect the autonomy and individual decision-making of a child without having him hop on the next train to California. First, however, we are going to look at the specific social code, or set of group expectations, that WED proposes.

JORDAN:
MODELING HEALTHY RELATIONSHIPS

After two days at Direction, Jordan had managed to offend nearly everyone in the program.

His seemingly incessant diatribes during group about the inferiority of non-Caucasian races (or anyone with skin darker with his) were made doubly troubling because Jordan was an articulate, intelligent, high-achieving boy who was well-read and backed up his claims of white superiority with extensive "research" he had done.

The fact that Jordan was perhaps the most blatantly racist client to come through the program might be attributed to an autistic-spectrum disorder with striking "black and white" (literally in this case) thinking. Whatever the cause, it became clear why this boy was depressed and angry: he had no real friendships and was disliked by virtually everyone.

A notable exception was our counselor Ric, which might seem odd because Ric is an African American man who grew up in the toughest of sections in New Orleans—with holes in his heart (and body) to prove it. Ric was a constant, direct target of Jordan's contempt in and outside of groups. Jordan even went so far as to take down Ric's license plate number to present to authorities if for some reason the need arose.

Ric, however, was the very picture of dignity, self-confidence, and compassion. He engaged Jordan in discussions of race. All the contempt, all the insults, rolled right off his back, as he never lost focus of his goal to help a boy with serious imbalances that were going to make for a very lonely life.

It's hard to tell what impact Ric ultimately had on Jordan, as Jordan was restricted from the group after a few weeks in the program and chose not to return. It is very unlikely, however, that Jordan had ever met someone like Ric, before or since. If anyone had a chance of influencing Jordan's world view, it was Ric.

One day while attending Direction, when his mother arrived to pick him up, and after a day of particularly intense "debate" with Ric, Jordan walked out the door. "Well, just don't expect me to ever like you," he said on his way out.

Jordan's mother was left facing Ric. She threw her arms around him and sobbed. "I'm so sorry. I didn't raise my boy to be that way!"

Ric smiled, "We've been talking all day.... I actually like him."

Gladly standing by as Ric wove his magic, Joe was prompted to comment, "And I'm glad you do too, because with those social habits, we gotta be the only two!"

TOM:
AVOIDING ADVERSARIAL DYNAMIC

"How bout I punch you in in the [expletive] face!" The sixteen-year-old spoke as slowly and clearly as he could, despite his severe speech impediment—the result of a traumatic brain injury that occurred fourteen years ago.

Joe was sitting in the room with Tom and had known him for about an hour. Unusually large for his age, Tom came across to most as a menacing, almost feral character, who had, in fact, punched a number of faces in the past. Underneath the anger and posturing, however, Joe was able to see a vulnerable, hurt child.

With a consciously casual posture, avoiding potentially threatening eye contact, Joe responded with a smile, "How 'bout we just be friends?"

Tom leaped from his chair and bolted out of Joe's office. His reaction was neither uncommon nor unexpected. Joe's genuinely caring response—and avoidance of being drawn into an adversarial dynamic—disarmed Tom and made Joe an entirely unsatisfactory object of further displaced anger.

In just a few minutes, Tom returned. Sitting back down in the same chair, he was a different person. Nonverbally inviting Joe to participate in his selective amnesia, Tom launched into a string of typical, mundane questions about the program.

Over the course of the next few weeks, Tom's truer self emerged. Joe never referenced his initial rudeness until months later, long after Tom had discarded his armor and laid down his arms, so to speak. To both parties, the incident had become just a humorous memory.

WED's Social Code:
The Behavioral Guidelines

"I'd just keep practicing the guidelines…"

—Joe Walsh, on how he would respond
if aliens landed in the parking lot

The Group's Social Code

At the heart of a group's culture is its social code. The social code can be thought of as the set of expectations group members have for one another. In most groups, including families, these expectations are implicit or "unwritten." They evolve on their own and remain in the background. Nevertheless, these codes of conduct are there: we can see them in the interactions between individuals and the conflicts that arise, and other aspects of group life that reveal what is considered "acceptable" behavior and what is not.

Ideally, social codes are in line with what we described as the attributes of a healthy group.

In particular, they should foster a positive spirit of collaboration, emphasizing mutual respect and cooperation. To that end, the social expectations should apply equally to all members. "Acceptable" social behavior is the same across the board. This isn't to say that leaders may not play a special role in the group, nor that parents may not have privileges that their children don't. It is simply to say that all are held to the same basic standard when it comes to social interactions. In the social code, you won't find George Orwell's line "But some animals are more equal than others."

Social codes should also allow individual liberty to the greatest extent possible ("minimum interference") while still preserving the structural integrity of

71

the group. A fundamental tension exists between all individuals belonging to any group. On one hand, we have the individual seeking the greatest freedom possible to pursue his or her own goals. On the other, we have the group's need for order and its pursuit of "the common good." Balancing the desires of the individual with the desires of the group is an age-old problem. Healthy groups have social codes strong enough to just strike this balance without becoming overly restrictive.

In other words, we want our social code to be short and sweet, yet comprehensive. It has to cover all the bases for social expectations but be minimally restrictive to individual autonomy.

We talked about most social codes evolving naturally in the background and being "implicit." WED proposes that the social code works better when made "explicit." It posits that it is important that the group's social code is in writing (rather than merely existing as informal, vague promises to be "decent" to each other), so there is a black-and-white description of what is expected of each member of the group. This avoids the problem of different group members following different social codes, or having different expectations from others. Knowledge that others are following the same social code is a prerequisite for trust.

WED submits the behavioral guidelines as such a social code. The code fits on one page. There is a second page that explains two of the terms used on the first page: "Wholeistic apology" and "Wholeistic leadership."

THE BEHAVIORAL GUIDELINES

1. **MAINTAIN AN ATTITUDE OF RESPECT AND DIGNITY.**
   a. Politely greet, welcome, and acknowledge efforts of all.
   b. Calmly request space if emotionally overwhelmed.
   c. Apologize for any possible offense, including accidents.*

2. **USE LANGUAGE AND THE BODY RESPONSIBLY.**
   a. Avoid offensive words, including those of a racial, ethnic, religious, or sexual nature.
   b. Refrain from using language or body to intimidate or injure.
   c. Calmly ask for an explanation of any confusion, disagreement, conflict, or concern.

3. **PROACTIVELY COOPERATE.**
   a. Seek opportunities to assist others, and resist urges to embarrass or undermine.
   b. Gratefully acknowledge the authority of leaders. **
   c. Treat all members as teammates, regardless of personal feelings.

4. **CAREFULLY ATTEND TO HEALTH AND SAFETY.**
   a. Alert an adult to any physical pain or danger.
   b. Control body movement such that self or others are not injured.
   c. Wear activity-appropriate clothing.
   d. Keep your body properly groomed (e.g., daily bathing, teeth brushing, etc.).
   e. Take good care of all furniture, equipment, facilities, and environment.

5. **HONESTLY GIVE YOUR BEST EFFORT.**
   a. Calmly communicate all perceived offenses.
   b. Earnestly participate in a just resolution of a dispute.
   c. Put education, wellness of self and others, and responsibility to the community ahead of personal image and interests.

* See "Wholeistic apology" on the next page
** See "Wholeistic leadership" on the next page

Wholeistic Apology

Wholeistic apology is true apology. It is a promise that although we did something wrong, we want to have a good relationship, and it is a concrete plan to prove that. Because wrongdoing is a natural part of being human, apologizing is something that everyone must do well.

To truly apologize, we do three things:

1. *Accurately understand what we did wrong. This means we must not minimize—for example, "Why are you making such a big deal of this?" That is criticizing the hurt person. Nor can we maximize—for example, "I'm the worst person in the world." That is an attempt to lower the expectations of others. Both are manipulative ways of avoiding responsibility.*
2. *Clearly communicate, "I am sorry"—and really mean it!*
3. *Make restitution. This is how we attempt to "repay" whomever we hurt, and fix or replace whatever we damaged.*

We can do the first step on our own, so we may find it relatively easy. If we accomplish that, the second step is often where the going gets tough. Do we have the strength to remain compassionate? Will we try to minimize or maximize when facing others? This can be especially hard if we have been hurt as well.

Even if we succeed at steps one and two, the third step usually involves some difficult moments. Making restitution can be a long and painful process because it's hard to know what it will take to re-earn trust. We may have to work at it long after we are again trustworthy and long after we feel we've proven it. So, in a way, whomever we apologize to has some control over us. This can make us feel afraid, sad, and angry.

But it's hard to truly apologize when we are full of our own feelings. Our emotions preoccupy us—we focus on ourselves, and usually place blame or responsibility on someone or something else. If we do that, even a little, we are not truly apologizing—and others will know it.

If, when we do wrong, we can really focus on caring for others and can truly apologize, even our wrongdoing can be transformed into an educational experience.

Wholeistic Leadership

Wholeistic leadership is gratefully acknowledging the leadership of whoever is most effectively practicing the behavioral guidelines at any given moment, regardless of age or other criteria. It is a powerful way to increase trust in the group. Wholeistic Leadership helps us prove that we are genuine in our commitment to practice the guidelines. Through our own honest practice, we become trustworthy group members and may lead by example.

That's all there is to the guidelines—nothing earth-shattering. Seems like just basic, decent human behavior, right?

The guidelines are based on good social habits that are applicable in virtually any group. So, in committing to the guidelines, we are not just reaping the benefits of belonging to the group; we are practicing better social habits and consequently improving our ability to function interpersonally within the context of other relationships as well.

When we implement WED in a group, the behavioral guidelines become our social code. At Direction, we require all individuals here (including the staff, who are also members of the group) to commit to the guidelines. We therefore all know what social behavior is expected from us as individuals, and what to expect from other group members.

We are using the same guidelines when we implement WED at home.

So we now have an explicit social code, and we know what is expected of all group members. Let's take a look at how we handle it when individuals in the group (such as our children) violate these expectations.

COMMITMENT TO THE GUIDELINES AND RESTRICTION

"I doubt that we can ever successfully impose values or attitudes
or behaviors on our children—certainly not by threat, guilt,
or punishment. But I do believe they can be induced through
relationships where parents and children are growing together. Such
relationships are, I believe, built on trust, example, talk, and caring."

—Fred Rogers

In WED, as long as individuals are committed to "practicing the guidelines," they are welcome in the group. We say "practicing" because everyone makes mistakes, and different people find different guidelines more difficult to follow. Acting the part of a mature adult isn't all that easy for adults, let alone children!

On the other hand, not being committed to the social code amounts to a decision to not be part of the group, as we discussed in an earlier chapter. Out of respect for the individual, and for the protection of the group, the group must accept this decision. "Not being committed" usually looks like an individual violating the guidelines repeatedly without demonstrating any effort to change his or her habits. Remember that actions speak louder than words, and the individual may protest loudly that he or she really wants to remain in the group while at the same time not showing any real effort. The individual is still making a choice, whether or not he or she verbalizes it as such, or whether or not he or she is happy with the consequences of leaving the group.

In WED, demonstrated noncommitment to the guidelines results in "restriction," or loss of access to all group privileges and resources. The restricted individual is no longer part of the group.

77

How, might you ask, is this any different from punishment or a "time-out"? For two reasons:

- It is the individual who has made the decision, by word or by deed, not to commit to the social code and therefore not to be part of the group.
- The person is welcome back at any time in the future, should he or she demonstrate a willingness to recommit to social code, through a process called "reintegration." There is no prescribed time of exclusion.

Often, being restricted from a group (such as in a family) *feels* like a punishment. Individuals like being part of healthy groups. (If the group wasn't healthy, of course, the individual might just as well be happier without the group.) They often miss the privileges, resources, and relationships they had in the group. Whatever consequences they face are natural, and any "punishment" that is experienced is in effect done by nature, not the group.

Restriction at Direction

The way we employ restriction at Direction may be illustrative to the reader.

First, we stress the voluntary nature of our program right off the bat, to both children and their parents, during the initial interview. Many children often come to their intake under the false presumption that we are going to decide for them whether or not they will join our program. They often think we are going to try to "force" them to come. We do our best to disabuse them of this notion as soon as possible, and sometimes we have to do the same for their parents. Children are often caught off guard at this point, because they are used to being told what to do. They usually are unsure how to process this stance into their world view of adults!

They may decide to join Direction because it is what they want to do. Or they may decide to join because they consider it to be a "less bad" option than the alternative, which might include disappointing or otherwise incurring consequences from their parents. Sometimes the court will "order" a child to attend our program. When they tell us they are "forced to come," we remind them that it's their choice still—it just may be a less bad choice from their perspective than the other option the judge gave them (e.g., placement at juvenile detention).

Whether or not a child "wants" to be at our program is ultimately irrelevant because we are ultimately focused on the behavior rather than the reason for the behavior. A child might hate coming to the program but nevertheless is welcome if he or she commits to the guidelines. Following the guidelines at the most basic level is a pretty easy thing to do. On the other hand, even a child who loves coming to the program is not welcome should he or she not demonstrate this commitment.

Because of the positive culture, and because our program is a pleasant place to be, children who initially hate the idea of coming frequently end up liking the program.

Restriction at Direction doesn't happen at the first sign of violation of the guidelines. What happens before and after restriction is the subject of the next chapter. Occasionally, however, a child demonstrates a lack of commitment to the point that he or she is restricted from the program. We simply ask the child to sit in the waiting area of the office and wait for his or her parents, whom we call. We emphasize to both the child and the parent that children are never "kicked out" of Direction. The child is welcome to return should he or she (not a parent) call us and request a "reintegration meeting." If the meeting is successful and the child convincingly recommits to our social code, he or she is welcome back.

Restriction at Home

Restriction from any outside group employing WED (e.g., a sports team or a classroom) looks pretty much the same as at Direction.

What about at home, however? If we implement WED, are we supposed to just let our fourteen-year-old child decide he doesn't want to belong to the family and take the next train out of town? It is true that parents are in an unusual position as group leaders in that they have a legal and ethical obligation to provide basic needs (e.g., food, shelter, care) for their children. So we really can't let that fourteen-year-old get on that train. However, there are other ways the child may effectively "leave the group," feeling respected and able to experience the positive and negative consequences thereof.

In a family, restriction usually looks like a child in his or her bedroom, without a cell phone, computer, TV, music devices, or any other group resource. The key here is that the child is busy learning, and it's every group member's duty (and hopefully desire) to help. So you must deny the child the most irresistible distraction at this point in time—*you*.

The parent or educator remains positive, loving, and kind, while he or she avoids the faintest appearance of interest in controlling the child. This also allows group energy to be retained in the group, best ensuring it remains an "oasis" to which the restricted member wants to return. In the meantime, we want to avoid interfering with the individual's experience and education.

For a child, virtually all valued things are group or family resources. Even if some devices may have been gifted to your child, or bought with his or her own money, it is highly unusual for a child to have paid for the electricity needed to run them. Also, trust is an invaluable group privilege, and the use of those devices may, in some cases, be rightly considered questionable, especially in light of the member's dissent. So, being housebound under the direct supervision of parents is only natural, seeing how parents have a legal and ethical obligation to ensure the safety and health of their children.

If the child refuses to move to a separate space, such as his or her room, or is in other ways not cooperative with restriction, he or she remains restricted. The child's consent to the restriction is irrelevant. Other family members do their best to ignore him or her, and deny all group privileges and resources (as always, excepting where safety and health are concerned).

You can see that the principle of restriction is the same at home as it is in any other group, like Direction, implementing WED. The complicating factor is the family has responsibilities to the child that other groups do not. We'll discuss how to approach the sometimes thorny issue of restriction at home in a later chapter.

Restriction is relatively uncommon at Direction and usually at home as well. Virtually everybody who restricts themselves asks for a reintegration meeting and successfully returns to the program. We do not view the restriction and reintegration process as being a setback or failure. Rather, it's part of the child's education and possibly even the child's most important experience while at our program.

The reason restriction doesn't happen more often is because there is a very deliberate, concrete process that occurs prior to the restriction that usually renders it unnecessary. This process is the subject of the next chapter.

THE FOUR RS

"Good judgment depends mostly on experience, and experience usually comes from poor judgment."

—Anonymous

This is where the action is, where we apply all the principles in the last chapter to conflict resolution within the group. This is also the most challenging part of WED.

WED is all about teaming up in mutual agreements to form common projects, thereby propelling WED's positive, educational culture. Lack of commitment is an issue we cannot overlook ("Neither punish nor enable"), as it undermines the integrity of the group. As will be discussed in a subsequent chapter, in addition to direct violation of the guidelines, there can also be violation of the Guidelines "in spirit." More on that later.

How does the group leader approach suspected violations of the guidelines? By using the four Rs.

The four Rs are *reflect*, *remind*, *restrict*, and *reintegrate*. They are the means by which WED approaches conflict in the group.

At Direction, we use the four Rs all the time. Usually we only get through the first one or two before things are sorted out, but sometimes a group member demonstrates a real lack of commitment to the guidelines and we have to move on to restriction (and hopefully reintegration).

It is important to note that the manner in which a group leader approaches the situation can make a huge difference as to how many Rs we go through. Often, after simple reflection, it becomes clear that we need go no further. Or another reminder may do the trick. It may be tempting for those new to WED to charge ahead, out of anger, anxiety, or just lack of experience, and blow through the first two Rs right to restriction.

Here's Joe, walking us through the four Rs in more detail and providing an example of the process.

WHAT ARE THE FOUR RS?

Reflect

- *Be sensitive and aware—embrace all feelings. When we have a strong feeling, we don't react—we pause, count to ten, and think.*
- *We remind ourselves of our commitment to practice the guidelines before reminding others.... Our spirit must reflect our commitment.*
- *We ask ourselves, "Has a behavioral guideline really been violated?" (We reread them if necessary.) If not, there may be no need to remind others.*
- *If there has been a significant violation of the guidelines ...*

Remind

- *Reminders are humble questions.*
- *We remind our teammate(s) of our mutually agreed upon practice.*
- *Reminders lead the group back to the group "mind"—they promote the practice of the guidelines.*
- *We resist any urge to control—no lectures, or orders—only humble questions!*
- *We all rely on reminders to become educated.*
- *Even when lovingly reminded, members may demonstrate a lack of commitment to the guidelines. If this is the case, continue with...*

Restrict

- *If a member is not committed to our practice we must accept, however regretfully, that they have restricted themselves from the group.*
- *Anyone who will not commit must discontinue contact with the group and give up all group privileges and resources (other than those necessary for safety and health).*

- *Restriction is not punishment! It is (a) proof of the group's respect for autonomy; (b) reassertion of the group's non-negotiable commitment to the guidelines; and (c) how the group protects itself from negative influences (specifically, people who are not practicing the guidelines).*
- *Because we still love those who reject the guidelines, we want their full education—so we must not interfere with their full experience of what it means to leave the group.*
- *It can be hard to avoid punishing the restricted member—remember, we neither enable nor punish!*
- *Restriction is not time-based; it's only about one's commitment to practice.*
- *When a restricted member genuinely requests to reenter the group...*

Reintegrate

- *This should be done as soon as possible, to avoid any unnecessary punishment of the restricted member.*
- *The reintegration meeting's sole function is to confirm the restricted member's genuine commitment to practice the guidelines.*

AN EXAMPLE OF THE FOUR RS: WED IN ACTION

Let's set the stage: I'm running a group for about twelve adolescents. I notice one client, Ann, refer to another, Patricia, as "stupid." I'm concerned that Ann's action may represent a violation of the group's social code—the guidelines—and it is my responsibility as a group leader to address this.

I start with the first R:

1. Reflect

I start by taking note of and embracing my feelings, which is something we should all make a habit of doing. When we have an uncomfortable feeling, it's best to pause for a moment to ensure that we don't react hastily or recklessly.

Reflection is time is to remind ourselves of our nonnegotiable commitment to practice the guidelines. We should respond (choice based), not react (impulse based), so that we avoid the temptation to control, punish, enable, or participate in the conflict. We should remind ourselves before we remind others!

I ask myself a couple of questions. Has a behavioral guideline really been violated? (For new practitioners of WED, reread the guidelines them if you aren't sure!) Have I really been wronged? Sometimes our own state of mind leads us to be more critical than we should be.

In the above example, perhaps I feel an immediate urge to criticize Ann. After some reflection, I realize that I'm still angry at her for something she did previously. Her referring to Patricia as "stupid" seems to have been said in jest and without any obviously intended offense, so perhaps the insult is relatively harmless. I decide to let it go and monitor the situation.

We need to remain true to our emotions and not try to hide them. We need to be genuine. Moreover, whenever our own behavior possibly strays from the guidelines, we have an excellent opportunity to model responsibility, Wholeistic apology, and self-forgiveness. If, for example, if I realized that I, in fact, did react rashly and criticize Ann without proper reflection, I might say to her: "I think I offended you. I'm really sorry. I feel like I'm getting frustrated and not practicing the guidelines as I should. I promise to do better. I know I can. Can you give me another chance? Can we please continue?"

If, on the other hand, upon reflection I decide that my concern about the comment was warranted, and I'm not being unfair, I ask myself: Does the behavior I am seeing reflect an unhealthy pattern or habit for Ann?

Let's say I conclude that I'm not being unfair to Ann, and although the word "stupid" is relatively mild and not obviously intended to offend, I think that in this instance the term may represent some real disrespect and attempt to embarrass Patricia. In my dedication to practicing the guidelines, I have an obligation to address this issue, so I'll move on to the next R....

2. Remind

If we believe the behavior should be addressed, we should remind. That is, we lead ourselves, and the group, back to the "mind" of the group practice. How can the group be sure what that practice is? Fortunately, we've got the guidelines, to which every group member has made a nonnegotiable commitment. I say to Ann: "Sorry to interrupt. I don't want to be a bother, but I think you might have hurt Patricia's feelings by calling her 'stupid.' What do you think?"

The manner in which we remind is critical. We must resist any urge to control by criticizing, lecturing, or ordering. Reminders come in the form of humble questions. Depending on our tone and body language, our questions can imply a gentle suspicion of wrongdoing or be a clear criticism, so we must remain pure of heart. If we do, our questions will communicate our belief in the person's capacity to accept responsibility without further external guidance.

We furthermore should remember to lead the discussion toward our shared guidelines and away from conflict between group members. It's easy to become distracted by the details of the events and lose sight of the bigger issue: our relationships and mutual commitment to working together.

Let's say Ann offers some kind of genuine and sufficient expression of responsibility. I praise her response and attempt to ease her discomfort. I say, "Oh, that's OK. It's not really a big deal. I'm really glad to see you practice the guidelines. Is there something you'd like to do to help make things better?"

Reinforcing healthy practice will make it more likely to become a habit. I may ask Ann if she believes that she should apologize, has she not done so. However, I must be careful not to undermine the member's success with a critical tone.

Even if this the millionth time we've gone over the same issue, we must remain hopeful in the potential growth of each group member!

Alternatively, let's say Ann responds to my question in a reasonably appropriate fashion but rejects the implied wrongdoing. I praise Ann for responding reasonably. If her answer satisfies my concerns, I might respond: "Thanks for explaining it to me so politely; now I get it. I'm sorry if I seemed too critical. Have I upset you?" Or, if it doesn't satisfy my concerns, "Well, thanks for talking to me about this politely, but I still don't understand.... Can you help me?"

By always expressing my concern only with reference to the guidelines and in the form of humble questions, I reduce the ability of the other member to displace attention from her behavior to ours and thereby reduce the possibility for conflict.

A significantly negative reaction to my humble question (e.g., "What's the big deal? Why can't you let this go!") means the relationship is currently too stressed to continue discussing the original event in question. I must therefore abandon my original question to refocus on our relationship.

I shift to humble questions about the inappropriate reaction to my question. We should never allow the past or future (the conflict or potential conflict being explored) to become more important than our practice in the moment—our teaming up. I ask, with no sarcasm or passive-aggressiveness, "Why are you speaking to me with that tone and giving me that angry look? Have I done something to offend you? I'm truly sorry if I have. I'm just concerned you may not be practicing the guidelines. Remember about avoiding offensive language in the guidelines? Can you please help me understand?"

Until we resolve the negative reaction to these humble questions, successful resolution of the original issue is highly unlikely. Teaming up is my constant focus. Important discussions about the facts and meaning of any conflict can be addressed in due time.

I continue triangulating the discussion with the guidelines, first in review of my behavior and then hers.

If I ultimately believe that Ann may not presently commit to practicing the guidelines, I might gently urge a temporary separation (see Guideline 1.b). I might calmly ask Ann to remove herself to a safe location until sufficient resources are available to further review the conflict.

3. Restrict

If, at this point, Ann will not separate voluntarily, or otherwise continues to demonstrate a lack of commitment to the guidelines (that's commitment, not compliance—being human, we must always expect errors of compliance), Ann has restricted herself from the group. As difficult as that may be to accept, I must. I must not inter-fere with Ann's experiencing the full weight and consequences of her decision to leave the group. So, I require that Ann discontinue contact with the group and to give up all group privileges and resources (other than those necessary to meet our legal and ethical responsibilities).

The guidelines have been adopted by the group as nonnegotiable, so if one chooses not to practice with the group, the group has not only the right but the duty to protect itself from the potentially negative influences of that dissenting member's behavior.

I say, as calmly and lovingly as possible, "Regretfully, I must accept that you're not practicing with our group right now, and that you've restricted yourself from the group. Please go sit at the front of the office, and we'll call your parents to come pick you up. I hope you will decide our group is good to belong to and ask for a reintegra-tion meeting soon."

Aside from any legal and ethical duties, those will be the last words I will speak to that person, until they decide to practice with the group and request a reintegra-tion meeting.

The analogy I like to use in parenting group is the following: Suppose I quit my job today. I can't just stroll in to work, three weeks later, hang out and chat with my friends, and then stop by the front desk for my paycheck, right? Lesson: when one leaves the group, one cannot demand access to the group and group resources, rights, and privileges.

We must remember that restriction is not punishment! It is a display of the group's respect for the autonomy of the dissenting member to reject the guidelines and, simultaneously, a reassertion of the group's nonnegotiable commitment to the guidelines. Because I do not seek control of others, I must allow members to leave the group. And because I love them, I must help ensure they experience all of the educa-tional consequences of their decisions.

Because we live in a "reward and punishment" based society, when accepting restriction, it can be hard to avoid punishing. A common mistake made by parents or other group leaders is to choose to deprive a restricted member of only one or a few group resources or privileges. (At home, this might be simply taking a cell phone away.) This would be an example of attempting to control by punishing in a way that may motivate the correct behavior, rather than respecting a person's decision to leave the group. By removing all, instead of some, group resources, we are providing the restricted member the most complete and realistic experience of what it means to leave a group.

We know and are relying on the fact that although loving restriction may feel punishing, it is nature that is applying the punishment—not us! This "punish-ment by nature" is primarily due to the intolerable discomfort of restriction deeply encoded in the human brain from hundreds of thousands of years of evolution. That is, humans are naturally selected to feel intolerant of restriction due to the fact that for much of our history, restriction from the group nearly always meant death.

Also, more mundanely, restriction feels punishing due to the unpleasant nature of being deprived the group's special, material provision (e.g., children at home want electronics!).

We prove that we are not punishing the group member in part by readily accepting him or her back into the group as immediately as practically possible upon the member's genuinely expressed recommitment to practicing the guidelines. This is the sole purpose of reintegration—the fourth "R." We do not impose a time frame on the restriction—that would once again be punishing.

In our current example, I communicate to Ann that the separation is not punitive, is hopefully temporary, and that I look forward to the opportunity to reintegrate her back into the group as soon as possible. I may temporarily close a door on group members, but they need to know that even if they find it locked, they hold the key!

4. Reintegrate

Here is a very important point in WED: we must wait for the dissenting member to voluntarily seek reintegration by earnestly asking for a reintegration meeting. Even if it is painful for us to witness the individual in distress, we are not fully respecting his or her autonomy if we try to cajole him or her into a reintegration meeting. We wait for the individual to ask for a reintegration meeting. If we believe the request is sincere, we grant this meeting as soon as feasible.

The sole purpose of the meeting is to reaffirm the individual's desire to rejoin the group and recommit to the guidelines. Usually a representative of the group (a parent, group leader, or even more ideally, the group as a whole) meets with the member and is charged with the task of making a judgment call about whether a restricted member genuinely desires to rejoin the group. Is the reintegration meeting confirming or disconfirming the commitment of the restricted member? Should the restricted member be reintegrated, or should the meeting be ended and the member remain restricted?

In preparation for the reintegration meeting, I think about how I could have shown greater leadership. I begin all meetings with a genuine apology. After all, if I were a better leader, perhaps we would have been able to have headed trouble off earlier. Remember, strong leaders invite criticism!

I ask the restricted member to review the guidelines first to explore and indicate any ways that I or others may have violated the guidelines. I proceed slowly and carefully, and help with the exploration when needed.

I must stress how important it is for all in the group to understand their potential mistakes so they may be better group members, and how we rely on each other for our education, in part, through loving criticism. I must take as much time as necessary to fully exhaust all of the restricted member's thoughts and feelings about how well others in the group are committed to the guidelines.

I must make a Wholeistic apology for any possible wrongdoing.

Assuming the restricted member has accepted my apology, I ask him or her to review the guidelines to explore his or her own potential violations. I gently ask for specific examples of violations of specific guidelines.

When the exploration is complete, I gently inquire about what the restricted member feels and thinks about these violations, and what he or she may like to do about those thoughts and feelings.

I gently introduce and promote the idea of Wholeistic apology if the restricted member does not. As welcomed, I assist in the process of Wholeistic apology. I focus especially on an effective plan of restitution.

I explore the possibility of better application of the guidelines, inviting questions, comments, criticisms, and any other thoughts and feelings.

I finish by confirming mutual commitment to practicing the guidelines, take any other appropriate course of action (e.g., assisting with restitution), and welcome the member back into the group in the most appropriately complete, warm, and loving way.

KATE:
PROVIDING CLEAR REFLECTION

Direction's third client ever, Kate, was immediately likable. A sixteen-year-old, energetic girl, Kate possessed the kind of charisma usually reserved for entertainers or politicians. She had a "big personality," with her open, bright energy, and seemed to always be the center of attention. In a group of only three clients that seemed like a blessing—until it didn't.

Kate's developmental imbalances soon came to the forefront. When group counselors attempted to break into Kate's seemingly incessant monologues with reminders such as "I'd like to hear what others think about x, y, or z. Wouldn't you?," she reacted with rude dismissal and continued disregard for others, further increasing her alienation from the group. When gently asked about the group's response to her, she would invariably escalate in anger, insisting, "This is just who I am, and I like who I am," "This group sucks," and other similar reactions of the best-defense-is-a-good-offense type. Most importantly, from the perspective of WED, Kate displayed that she was not "with" the group. She was not committed to the guidelines—the only nonnegotiable requirement of participation.

Just a day or two into our work, she had restricted herself. (Duncan at the time was still warming up to Joe's approach and was a more than a little alarmed that the census had been slashed by a third in the tenuous program's first week.)

Kate called for a reintegration meeting the next day. During the meeting, Duncan went about doing something he does well: finding common ground, diffusing tension, and seeking to reforge a therapeutic alliance. At one point he said that he knew that the group had gotten tense, that Kate may have overreacted, but that she herself wasn't the main reason that things had gotten so out of hand in the group.

At that point, Joe interjected, providing clear reflection. "Kate, I disagree. I think you are precisely the reason that the group has become so negative. Would you like to work on this with us?" Though Duncan hid it well, he was secretly cringing at Joe's directness (tactlessness, even).

Needless to say, at that time, Kate did not hide her feelings quite as well. She stormed out of the office, shouting that she was going to "wrap [her] car around a [expletive] tree!" After calling her mother and ensuring her safety, Kate was once again sent home, restricted.

However, the combination of Joe's directness and his and the group's clear caring for her—which doesn't take long to establish in a culture like Direction's—made an impression on Kate that would take a while for her to process.

About a month later, Kate called for a second reintegration meeting, which was successful. Her negative attitude in group had undergone a transformation, and she became one of the most positive influences in the group.

She finished the program without a further hitch and has been back to visit many times over the years, even while on break from college. She later would credit Direction for helping her wake up to the reality her own bad habits—and change them for the better.

WHOLEISTIC EDUCATION SUMMARY

"Pills never taught a person a damn thing."

—Dave Gill, MD

We've covered a lot of WED theory in the last few chapters. Congratulations if you've made it this far! Now we are going to try to piece things together and paint a coherent picture of how WED creates healthy groups and can help at home.

Here's what we have so far:

- **A set of principles for group leaders**
  - *Model healthy relationships*
  - *Provide clear reflection*
  - *Encourage true focus*
  - *Give up control to gain authority*
  - *Neither punish nor enable imbalanced behavior*
  - *Avoid adversarial dynamic*
  - *Embrace all feelings, guide all behavior*

  These principles emphasize leadership by example and respect for autonomy.

- **A social code for the group: the behavioral guidelines**
  The guidelines are a black-and-white, minimalistic set of expectations that group members commit to which both allow the greatest degree of freedom possible to individuals while safeguarding the common good and integrity of the group. You'll note that the guidelines emphasize cooperation, humility, and respect for each other. They also represent great habits to develop in terms of getting along with others in any relationship.

- **A system of conflict resolution**
  The four Rs are our method of evaluating individuals' commitment to our group's social code and guide us when a group member's commitment is called into question.

We now have the ingredients that we need to form a healthy group that has a cooperative spirit, promotes growth and development, and encourages good habits.

How do we put this into practice at home?

Applying Wholeistic Education at Home

"The best time to plant a tree is twenty years ago. The second-best time is now."

—Chinese proverb

The Process of WED Implementation

The parents we see who are willing to try implementing WED in their families are doing so for a reason: things aren't going well at home. Relationships are strained, people are arguing, kids are acting out or shutting down. It would have been great to have implemented WED before things got to this point, but hindsight is 20/20.

If you are one of those parents willing to take the leap, we are going to tell you how to do so.

First and foremost, you need to start with a gut check. Embarking on the implementation of WED means that you will be held to the same standards as your child. You will need to commit yourself to following the guidelines and working on your own bad relationship habits that may have been unattended to for years (or perhaps never attended to). Are you ready to make changes to your own behavior and improve your own habits? Are you ready to own your own shortcomings? Are you ready to apologize when you make mistakes? Are you ready to truly model healthy behavior? Furthermore, are you willing to go all the way? Will you tolerate your child's bad decisions? Will you get out from between them and their education? Will you make yourself obsolete? Will you have the nerve to call the police or an ambulance, if it comes to that?

If not, there is honestly no point in going further. WED will not work in this situation.

WED is front-loaded, much like a mortgage. At first, you pay more interest, gaining equity over time. It requires discipline, patience, and in most cases, faith.

On the other hand, if you are willing to put in the effort, humble yourself, and make these changes, you can proceed to the next step.

Like so many other aspects of WED, the next step involves doing something counterintuitive. We recommend that you start with an apology to your child (or children).

Why on earth would you start with an apology? You may be thinking at this point: "My child's the one who's been a complete jerk recently. Why should I apologize to him?"

While it's necessary to begin a reintegration meeting with your own apology (which we'll discuss in more detail later on), it's a nice way to start any discussion. Particularly when you are introducing a significant change. Even if it is a course correction.

We recommend starting with an apology for a few reasons. The first is that you can usually look back on your own behavior and see at least some way you have contributed to the problem. This is an excellent time to begin "Modeling Healthy Relationships," even if you don't get an apology in return. (Don't hold your breath!) The second is that even if you cannot see how your behavior has contributed to the conflict, it is quite likely it has in some fashion. After all, the "perfect parent" (or "perfect group leader") would have either prevented the conflict entirely or headed it off earlier. Of course, none of us are perfect parents, and acknowledging this fact right at the start can be very helpful. It models humility. Moreover, as the implementation of WED proceeds, you may well discover ways that you have unwittingly conspired to create a negative family culture.

Here's what an apology might look like prior to implementing WED:

"John, I know things haven't been going well for us at home recently. I would like to apologize for the ways I may have made things worse. [Great time to insert something specific, like 'yelling too much,' 'being too controlling and/or punitive,' or 'being inattentive.'] I think I can do a better job as a parent, and promise I'm going to do my best to change, so hopefully our relationship improves. I have some ideas I'd like to discuss with you. Can we do that?"

After the apology, you are ready to go about the business of implementing WED.

You simply gather all family members and review the behavioral guidelines, Wholeistic apology, and Wholeistic leadership. Your family reviews and discusses anything that seems to be objectionable or omitted. There rarely is much discussion at this point, because there's not a whole lot to object to. Each family member affirms commitment to the guidelines, which will serve as the social code for the family from that point on. Note that parents, as group leaders, need to commit to the same set of expectations as everyone else.

Your decision as a parent to implement WED at home—and the behavioral guidelines—is the one nonnegotiable element of Wholeistic Education.

That's it. WED is "implemented." From here on out, the family commits to the practice of the guidelines, principles of WED, and system of conflict resolution (the four Rs).

How WED Works in a Family: An Analogy

Though the guidelines may be the heart of WED, they need to be put into context within the family structure.

For purposes of illustration, let's consider the implementation of WED to be analogous to a family's moving into a new house. Any house we would want to live in has a solid foundation, sturdy framing for the walls and roof, and a finished interior. Here's how these specific elements can be viewed through the lens of WED:

1. **The foundation: basic safety at home**
   Walls and interior decorating don't mean much when your house is sliding into the swamp. Establishing your home as a safe place for all is of primary importance. A safe home serves as the foundation on which all else is built, without which nothing else will work. This means no violence or threats of violence at home, either to self or to others. If our home is unsafe, making it so is our number-one priority.

2. **The framing: the behavioral guidelines and four Rs**
   Framing holds up the walls and roof, giving the house its structure. There is little point in thinking about the interior and wall decorations if the roof is leaking. The guidelines address relationships in the moment and guide us through social interactions as they occur. Family problems and conflict inevitably arise and at times strain relationships. The guidelines and four Rs are how we work through these conflicts as they occur.

3. **Interior design: proactive planning**

   Assuming a solid foundation, walls, and roof, we can start thinking about the inside of the house and making it our own. "Proactive planning" is the process by which family members make concrete plans as to how they are going to achieve certain goals, manage stresses and resources, and divide chores among family members. Proactive planning may also mean agreements between family members as to how to move forward in the face of differences of opinion. The key word here is "proactive"—as opposed to "reactive." An ounce of prevention is worth a pound of cure, as they say.

The idea is that we end up with the solid, livable house we want—literally and figuratively.

Let's look at these three structural elements in greater detail.

THE FOUNDATION OF
YOUR HOME: SAFETY

"When the train is coming, you don't wait—you pull your child off
the tracks."

—Joe Walsh, LCMHC

When it comes to immediate safety, parents need to take charge. This is an
exception to the WED axiom "seek not to control." It is important to do so
swiftly, efficiently, and deliberately—and, for reasons that will be explained,
as dispassionately as possible. As parents, we likely will feel strong emotions
while responding to safety emergencies at home. While it is important to
embrace those feelings, in these situations it is critical not to dwell on them
but focus on guiding behavior. There is time for dealing with the emotions
once the crisis is over. Think of the cool-headed soldier in battle.

As a parent, this means seriously responding to all potential threats to
health and welfare of any family member. This includes violence or threats
of violence against others (e.g., the child who shoves his mother or begins
destroying furniture), as well as violence toward self (e.g., the child who
threatens suicide or attempts suicide).

How do we deal with these situations?

In general, the response should be either a trip to the emergency room or
a call to 911.

If a child immediately walks back on a verbal threat, and is absolutely
100 percent convincing, we might be able to avoid going this route. But the
onus is on the child, not the parent, to do the convincing.

Any true act of violence towards others or significant damage to property
warrants a call to the police. Any suicide attempt warrants a trip to the ER (if
the child is willing to go) or a call to 911 (if the child is not). The same holds

true for children who cannot be entirely convincing that a threat to himself or others was made out of anger and not genuine. If in doubt, err on the side of caution.

A big mistake some parents make is not taking threats of suicide or statements about having attempted suicide seriously. They often think their children are "just being manipulative."

"Just being manipulative," when referring to suicidal statements or actions, may mean a lot of things, but most parents use the phrase when they believe a child is acting out "to get attention." Usually the idea is that the child is trying to make a statement to others and has no true intent of dying. And, in fact, this is often the case.

There are, however, a number of problems in this line of thinking—that because an action was "manipulative," it should be ignored or not taken seriously:

1. Children who are in fact "being manipulative" kill themselves by accident.
2. Children "looking for attention" may be angry or upset enough with a parent, peer, school system, or the world that they really *do* want to die to get their message across. Or at least they don't care in the moment if they live or die.
3. "Being manipulative" or "looking for attention" may only be part of the story for a kid who has a biological imbalance such as depression or bipolar disorder.
4. No matter how sure we feel, it is ultimately impossible to truly know the motivation of the child's action.

What are we to do as parents?

The simplest, most reliable solution is to regard the motivation as irrelevant to the response, which is getting our child to the ER.

In the case of expressed suicidality or suicide attempt, what our recommended approach accomplishes is the following:

- It demonstrates beyond a shadow of a doubt that we care about our children and won't take chances with their safety.
- It demonstrates beyond a shadow of a doubt that we take everything they say seriously and that their words matter.
- It demonstrates beyond a shadow of a doubt that we are taking charge as parents, going from talk mode ("embracing all feelings") to action mode ("guiding all behaviors").

- It simplifies the situation to an "if-A-then-B" algorithm—one that doesn't require a lot of thinking or agonizing.
- In the case of the child who is solely "being manipulative," it avoids our being held hostage by suicidal threats or actions.
- It gives us the opportunity to prove to a potentially "manipulative" child that our response is going to be consistent and dispassionate. Going to the ER can be a real pain. We want them to believe (correctly) that they will get tired of it before we do.
- It takes us out of an adversarial dynamic with our child. If he or she is truly "seeking attention" and does not want to be hospitalized, but rather wants to "make a point," he or she can debate with the with a clinician in the ER rather than us. This experience alone may dissuade a child from engaging in the same routine next time.
- It avoids potential escalation at home by a child who feels his or her threats are being ignored, which often leads the child to "up the ante" and engage in more dangerous behavior.
- It may save your child's life. You might be wrong about our child's motivation. You might be grossly underestimating the actual risk of suicide. As clinicians, we been doing this for many years and are humble enough to know that we get it wrong sometimes.

We see these benefits—even if a child is sent home—as far outweighing the hassle and expense of a trip to the emergency room.

For violence or threats of violence at home, we provide the following reasons for calling 911:

- It demonstrates beyond a shadow of a doubt that we care about our children and won't take chances with their or other family members' safety.
- It demonstrates beyond a shadow of a doubt that we take everything they say seriously, and that their words and actions matter.
- It demonstrates beyond a shadow of a doubt that we are taking charge as parents and going from talk mode ("embracing all feelings") to action mode ("guiding all behaviors").
- It simplifies the situation to an "if-A-then-B" algorithm, and doesn't require a lot of thinking or agonizing.
- It avoids the trap of being held hostage by threats of violence. It stops the cycle of demands being backed by the implication of violence. It stops us from having to "walk on eggshells" at home.
- It takes us out of an adversarial dynamic with our child. Let him or her argue it out with the police (or the judge). Remain an oasis, to which

your child will want to return. This experience alone may dissuade a child from engaging in the same routine next time.

- It avoids potential escalation at home by a child who feels his or her threats are being ignored, which often leads the child to "up the ante" and engage in more dangerous behavior.
- It avoids our succumbing to the temptation to become involved physically with a child (e.g., restraining the child or actually physically fighting with him or her), which is an absolutely terrible idea that violates virtually every principle of WED, including avoiding adversarial dynamic, seeking not to control, avoiding punishment, modeling healthy relationship, and so forth.

Parents often express certain worries when it comes to calling 911 when their children are being violent at home.

- *"It will make them angry!"*
  Fine. This is the time to be a parent. We aren't in the feel better business, as we've said. They are far less likely to be violent next time (despite being angrier), given their experience with law enforcement and perhaps the legal system.

- *"It will go on their permanent record!"*
  Not necessarily—this varies from state to state, and juvenile records are often expunged at the age of eighteen. Regardless, it is far better for them to experience real societal consequences of their actions as children rather than as adults. The earlier these habits can be broken, the better.

- *"My child will be taken away from me!"*
  Very unlikely. States and courts don't have a lot of money to spend on alternative living arrangements for children. In addition, if your child actually commits serious enough infractions to be placed into detention or a residential facility for a period of time, it is very likely the best course of action for him or her.

- *"It's admitting failure, embarrassing, and will get the neighbors talking!"*
  This is putting your own wants and needs ahead of your child's.

Responding to Further Chronic Self-Destructive Behavior

So that's the algorithm for emergencies: 911 or ER trip. Pretty simple.

The algorithm for nonemergencies is simple as well: follow the principles of WED.

The hard part is distinguishing between what is an emergency and what is not. Sometimes it comes down to a judgment call. As we said, err on the side of caution. However, there are plenty of self-destructive things children do that do not always constitute an emergency. A couple of examples might include superficial cutting or eating-disorder behavior.

We need to say up front that there are different reasons and different levels of danger in these types of behavior. Some youth who cut themselves (e.g., ones with bipolar disorder, schizophrenia, or severe trauma) do so in ways that are truly life-threatening—regarded as suicide attempts. Some eating disorders (particularly severe anorexia) so distort a person's thinking that he or she requires hospitalization for malnutrition and potentially fatal consequences. Again, the maxim holds true: if in doubt, err on the side of caution—get your child to the ER—as dispassionately as possible.

For many other children, however, superficial cutting, eating-disorder behavior, and similar habits represent developmental imbalances and bad habits.

The main problem that we encounter is that these types of behavior invite a power struggle between children and their parents. In effect, the normal biological drive of the child to seek independence has found an unhealthy outlet. Parents often fall into the trap of taking the bait and violating the key WED principles:

1. *Give up control to gain authority.*
   The desperate, frightened parent often will seek to control his or her child, often with the encouragement of well-meaning but misguided therapists. Parents will try to "lock up all the sharps" or conduct "body checks" to keep children from cutting. Think about it: if a child really wants to cut, he or she will find to do so. (We view access to firearms or medication a child could potentially overdose on as being a different animal, given the immediacy of lethality, and always recommend these things be kept secure.) Parents will try to "force" their children to eat. We do not recommend these approaches, because they violate the above principle. Struggling for control invariably leads to violating the second principle:

2. *Neither punish nor enable.*

Specifically, if we engage in the power struggle and try to control our children, we are enabling them by absolving themselves from responsibility for their own actions. We are giving them the message that they are incapable of changing behavior, which we have discussed, is rarely the case (recall Joe's billion-dollar question: *"If I had thirty million dollars to give you if you didn't do 'x,' could you keep from doing it?"*). We are making the mistake of fostering dependence, not promoting independence.

3. *Avoid adversarial dynamic.*

Once we engage in adversarial dynamic, we've compounded one problem (the behavior itself) with at least two others: depriving our child of the full educational benefit of his or her decision by presenting an irresistible distraction (us!), and degrading the positive group culture. Most importantly, we've stopped working as a team. Telling your child that you are going to force him or her to stop is a surefire way to encourage a maladaptive behavior.

In most instances, these types of bad habits should be viewed as maladaptive responses to stress. The behavior itself is usually secondary to a more fundamental imbalance, which is where we should focus our efforts.

A final point: in dealing with both biological and developmental imbalances, we are always trying to weigh relative risks. The risk of a child's cutting, for example, might indeed be reduced in the short term by "locking up sharps" or conducting "body checks." However, we need to remember that in doing so, we are taking a different risk. In our violation of the basic principles listed above and the consequent impact on our relationship with our child, we may be prolonging (or worsening) the problem in the longer term, and doing the child more harm than good.

The reader may think that we are giving mixed messages here. On one hand, we are saying to bring your child to the ER for dangerous statements or actions. On the other hand, we are telling parents not to control, to neither punish nor enable, and to avoid adversarial dynamic.

In fact, we are trying to reduce our responses to a single algorithm that violates the principles of WED as minimally as possible. In an emergency (your child is lying on the train tracks), we *do* seek to control. (Note that we are still following the other two axioms: we are avoiding adversarial dynamic and neither seeking to enable nor punish.) If we aren't facing an emergency, we are following all three principles (including seeking not to control).

Framing:
The Behavioral Guidelines and Four Rs in the Family

"A house divided against itself cannot stand."

—Abraham Lincoln

We've been over the behavioral guidelines (WED's social code) and four Rs (WED's response to conflict). They deal with relationships as they occur (in group therapy speak, the "here and now"). We treat other family members well, view them as teammates, ask humble questions, and communicate perceived offenses. We practice good relationship habits and start to get along better because of it.

In reality, however, there's often a lot of catch-up work to do when we first institute WED, because dynamics may already be adversarial, habits and unhealthy family patterns entrenched, and there exists a plain-old negative vibe. Not only that, but a lot of the principles in WED are foreign to many people, so implementing them will feel unnatural and challenging. The learning curve may be steep. And our children may say, "Hey—I never signed up for this!"

Often, things get worse before they get better. It is important to remember, however, that we are constantly trying to get our children to learn to delay gratification. As parents, in implementing this system, we need to be prepared to do so as well and practice what we preach.

It's generally best to just jump in. The road will be bumpy at first, but if the family sticks with it, it likely will smooth out over time.

105

Starting to Practice Humble Questions

We begin by practicing replacement of statements of judgment (even if fact), pronouncements, and any tempting sarcastic remarks with humble questions. Humble questions are far less likely to be seen as provocative and inflame dynamics that may be already adversarial. (In addition, it's hard to respond to a humble question in a sarcastic, provocative manner without appearing to be a real jerk.) It's a great way to start modeling healthy relationships as a parent.

Moving Sequentially through the Four Rs

If we believe our social code is being broken in some way, we always begin with *reflect* (the first 'R' is not "react"!). Is a guideline truly being violated? Note that "doing homework" or "cleaning your room" aren't guidelines—they'll come later in the next chapter. The guidelines have to do with interactions occurring in the present. How is your child talking to you? Is he or she acknowledging (and hopefully apologizing for) perceived offenses, even if unintentional? Even more importantly, are you apologizing for perceived offenses and modeling healthy relationships?

We move to the second 'R' if it becomes apparent a guideline is being violated. The second R, *remind*, always comes in the form of humble questions. The first humble question should nearly always be something to the effect of, "I've got something on my mind. Can I have a moment of your time?" As parents, we are probably used to the idea that our children must speak with us whenever we want. By beginning without any such expectation, we are letting our child know that we are practicing a new way—a way in which we will not seek control over them. "I couldn't help but find that language offensive that you just used. Do you remember my mentioning that before?" Any acknowledgment of wrongdoing by your child is a good start. We must be prepared to offer more reminders in the future, as sometimes habits take some time to change. All reminders should be made in reference to the guidelines—that's what reminders are for.

If reminders are insufficient, and a child demonstrates he or she is not committed to following the guidelines, it's time to move to *restriction*. This is when we regretfully accept his or her autonomous decision to not follow the code and restrict him or herself. It's only natural. We even expect houseguests to conform to our basic house "rules" or leave. You don't just let any old stranger plop in front of your TV and raid the fridge, do you?

If at any point during restriction the child demonstrates a desire to return to the group and would like to reaffirm commitment to the guidelines, a reintegration meeting should be held as soon as feasible. If he or she truly can demonstrate commitment, we should warmly welcome our child back into the group.

If a Child Refuses to Acknowledge Restriction

Restriction is the group's honoring a member's autonomy and decision to not be part of the group. As Joe explained in a previous chapter, at home restriction of a child generally looks like his or her being in her room without access to group resources, which are…pretty much everything (e.g., phone, books, laptops, the car, etc.). Of course, exceptions are made for primary needs that parents must provide (e.g., food, clothing, shelter, medical care, etc.). This may seem pretty severe, but recall that the child is welcome back into the group anytime he or she chooses to recommit to the guidelines.

What do we do if a child won't "accept" restriction? Here's Joe's answer:

Say that we have informed a child that we've accepted his restriction, and he tells us in an unfriendly tone where we can shove those guidelines (not uncommon), and that he's not going to his room, and he's not giving up his cell phone, and so on.

That confirms that we made the proper observation that the person had, in fact, left the group, and is continuing to restrict himself or herself from the group. Other family members continue to have minimal contact with him or her. All group resources are returned to the group (without any adversarial dynamic). Under no circumstances should a parent initiate any kind of confrontation (e.g., trying to yank a cell phone away). On the other hand, should the child become physical or threatening, we return to our foundation of safety at home and call the police. Should a child threaten to kill himself or herself because of the restriction, we follow the same protocol. Safety first.

In terms of confiscating more group privileges a child is not willing to give up, there are a number of options. If a child goes to school the next day, things from his room can be confiscated then. Cell phone service and Wi-Fi can be turned off. The main thing is not to participate in the repeated attempts of the child to engage you in combat (metaphoric or otherwise). Avoid adversarial dynamic. Stay focused on the process, as politely, dispassionately, and lovingly as possible, and remember that restriction is not punishment but respect for autonomy; its enforcement is merely for the protection of the group.

If you accept restriction in the way we mean it, keep the group a "loving oasis," allow the child to feel the "full weight and consequences" of his decision to leave the group, and don't provide the counterproductive distraction of punishment or adversarial dynamic; the child will soon learn the error of his decision. Children come preprogramed to learn—if you can bear to get out of the way and let them do it! In the roughly thirty years that Joe has been using the four Rs, the longest time a (particularly troubled residential) child was restricted was about twenty-eight days. Virtually everyone else learns in just a few days. At some point, a child will become tired of being restricted and ask to be reintegrated. Or it's possible he or she will become so angry as to threaten his safety or the safety of someone else, and we already know how to deal with that.

INTERIOR DESIGN:
PROACTIVE PLANNING

"A goal without a plan is just a wish."

—Antoine de Saint-Exupéry

Now we've got a safe home and a solid social contract as to how we treat each other. We are now in a position to leverage the positive culture that we have established at home (or are establishing) to tackle family problems together with our children. This is a far preferable alternative to a more common pattern: parent tries to solve problem, parent pushes solution on child, child pushes back, repeat.

Easier Proactive Planning

If family members agree on a problem, proactive planning can be simple. Take the case of a child's wish to stop smoking (or, for that matter, a parent's wish to stop smoking). The family comes up collaboratively with a proactive plan to help this individual in his or her efforts to stop. Maybe it's the family's talking with the primary care doctor about medical options. Maybe it's the child's agreeing to give up and discard cigarettes in his or her possession. Maybe it is just the simple emotional support provided by other family members. Of course, this assumes the child (or parent) truly has the desire to stop.

At Direction, proactive planning might involve the group's helping a member deal with an unhealthy relationship with a peer. The group may suggest blocking the peer on social media (or, better yet, giving up social media altogether), or ignoring attempts by the peer to engage the child. For a child who feels like he is wasting his day on video games and becoming increasingly isolated, the group may help him come up with a concrete schedule to fill

109

his day with healthier activities that encourage getting out of the house and engaging in social interaction.

The point is that the family or group is working together to make proactive plans to address a particular problem, rather than waiting for things to "improve on their own." Or relying on dime-a-dozen "coping strategies" that work, to the degree they might, due to the power of novelty—their effectiveness fading like any fad diet. The positive family culture provides an energy that boosts efforts to implement the individual's plans. Other members cheer the individual's successes in his efforts and support him when he struggles.

More Difficult Proactive Planning

It gets harder when parents and children have different goals or agendas. We are entering the realm of questions we encounter in parenting group every week:

- *How do I get my child to go to school?*
- *How do I get my daughter to realize that her boyfriend is unhealthy for her?*
- *How do I get my son to get off the Xbox?*
- *How do I get my child to stop making bonehead decisions?*

We've gone over two common parental strategies that are unlikely to be met with much success:

- Ignoring the problem
- Trying to impose the parent's own solution on the problem

Both alternatives are inconsistent with the principles of WED. The first violates the principle of "Not enabling" and the second violates the principle of "Seeking not to control."

However, if we have established a healthy culture in the family, we've at least opened up the possibility of a third option:

- Working together to come up with an agreement

This third option is simply not available to the family or group with a negative culture. WED makes no guarantees that you and your child will come up with a mutually agreeable solution, which is why we tell parents we have no simple answers to questions such as these. We remind parents over and over that

WED is an approach, not a solution. If WED has been properly implemented and the culture sufficiently cooperative, however, the family has a real chance at working things out.

Agreements

Forming agreements with a child can be both powerful and difficult. It can be powerful in that it really emphasizes the family's collaborative, unified effort to solve problems. It can be difficult because parents and children may have very different perceptions of what are worthy goals to pursue, and the relative risks inherent in certain situations or actions (or inaction, for that matter). Because of the individual nature of the problems to be addressed, the different personalities and dynamics at play, and potential other complicating factors, we can only offer some guidelines in seeking agreements with children:

- Start discussions during a period of relative calm, not in the thick of conflict when emotions are running high. Make proactive plans as you can. Immediately following the implementation of WED is ideal, but be careful not to let your zeal for teaming up cause you to slip back into your controlling habits.
- Employ all the principles of WED discussed in previous chapters (e.g., ask humble questions, avoid adversarial dynamic, provide clear reflection, etc.) All these will minimize the chance of the child's becoming defensive and shutting down.
- Start with a point—any point!—of agreement. For example, "Is safe to say that we both agree that getting your high school diploma or equivalent is something that you want to do?"
- During the discussion, follow the guidelines.
- Move from the general areas of agreement to specific plans of action. This process may take a while, and may not be accomplished in one discussion. Consider positive movement at all a success and celebrate it as such.

One of the benefits of forming agreements with our children is that we get ourselves all "on record" as voluntarily committing to a particular plan of action. It's not as if the parent has simply come down with a decree (read: effort to control).

Consider an agreement we make with all clients starting at Direction. We discuss our concern about cell phone usage during the program: how it both isolates children and risks violating the confidentiality of the group. Virtually all children see these as logical, reasonable concerns and are willing to agree to keep phones "off and invisible" while in the program. But as we know, children love their phones, and frequently we find them sneaking in texting here and there.

We are now in a position to ask a humble question when we find children on their phones:

"Hey there—do you remember that agreement we made about using phones?"

This essentially is a reminder and invites cooperative discussion. We might get "Oops, I forgot," or "Sorry, won't happen again," or "That's a stupid policy." We then can take it from there.

If, on the other hand, we presented a decree of "No cell phone usage here," we'd be stuck with an "enforcement-type" (control-oriented) scenario.

"Hey, you can't use cell phones here."

No real room for further discussion, exploration. Feels like control.

Again, this may seem like semantics, but it's not. "Agreements" connote cooperation; "rules" connote control.

Handling Violations of Agreements

Agreements themselves aren't part of the behavioral guidelines. You won't find guidelines about video games, drugs or alcohol, or boyfriends. Rather, they represent the framework in which we can work to find common solutions. Joe describes the guidelines as a "matrix through which each group puts their own, unique stressors, resources, and values."

We can view agreements as being a "barometer" of our relationship and culture. Violations of agreements are often not overt violations of the guidelines "in word," but can signify an individual's lack of commitment to the "spirit" of the guidelines—cooperation with other group members. Not holding up one's end of the bargain is an indication of a problem in the relationship that requires attention.

Accordingly, repeated violations of agreements warrant discussion with the individual and possible modification of the agreement. Or it may demonstrate the individual's lack of commitment to the spirit of the guidelines and lead to restriction from the group.

Rules: Unilateral Parental Decisions

Here we come to our fallback position. There may be certain scenarios in which parents and children are so far apart in their values or positions on a problem as to render the problem insoluble. We've already encountered some of these problems in reviewing parental responses to actions threatening the safety of family members at home.

But what about other behavior that the parent may judge to be "bad" for a child? What about social media? Unmonitored access to the internet? Staying out the whole night? Driving-related concerns? Drug use? Hanging out with children who may be terrible influences?

We start as we always do, laying out our concerns, hearing our children out, and patiently and deliberately seeking common ground (e.g., "Can you see where I'm coming from in my concerns about you hanging out with Doug? Is there something we can do about that?"). Using the guidelines, humble questions, and the four Rs, we discuss our differences and do our best to seek an agreement that leaves us both (relatively, at least) satisfied.

Let's assume that, as a parent, we've patiently gone through this whole approach to no avail. There's no common ground to be found. Neither of you will budge.

It's time to ask ourselves a question: Do we judge the risk of the child's behavior as greater than the risk posed by interfering in the child's natural learning from experience?

The answer may be yes, or it may be no, depending on the issue at hand, what we know about our children, and our own family's values. Naturally, most parents are prejudicially in favor of their own position, and thus may need a trusted third and fourth opinion on this one.

If the answer is yes, we may decide that we need to make a unilateral decision as a parent and present it as such to the child. Ultimately, it's our ethical and legal responsibility as parents to raise healthy children.

If we do so, however, we need to know that we are taking the following risk: We are depriving our child the full educational benefit of learning from his or her own mistakes. We are "interfering," exerting control, and possibly creating adversarial dynamic. And we need to be prepared for the possibility that our child simply won't follow the rule.

Done in the right spirit ("I respect your opinion, but in my love and concern for you feel I have to make a decision in this case as the parent"), and as sparingly as possible, this may work out fine and be the best course of action. Regardless of the immediate "feedback" they may give, children can tell the difference when we as parents are intervening out of love from when we are seeking to control. As Joe often tells parents: "If you are really pure of spirit and follow the four Rs faithfully, most children will not begrudge your momentary control. Rather, they will be comforted by it."

One can see that we have a far better chance at a positive outcome if we have established a positive culture at home, have a good relationship with our child, and see "rules" as the exception rather than the rule, so to speak.

The Seductiveness of Interference

"Good parenting: maximum support, minimum interference."

—Jock Gill, MD

It is inevitable that our children will make bad decisions. Having been children ourselves, having lived many more years, and having made many more mistakes than our children, we may well be right about a decision being a bad one. In some cases, we might be wrong. As parents, we need to do our best to minimally interfere with our children's education. As Joe puts it, "We must not deprive children of the maximum educational benefit of their decisions."

We can provide counsel, model healthy relationships, come up with agreements, and even make certain unilateral decisions (rules) for our children. Nevertheless, despite our best efforts, sometimes children are going to just do their own thing. This is part of their march toward independence. They sometimes are just going to need to make their own mistakes. Occasionally, they'll prove us wrong.

We've discussed certain instances requiring the parent's simply taking control (e.g., in matters of serious threat to safety). We've discussed restriction in the context of violation of both the letter and spirit of the guidelines.

Other than that, we are looking for "maximum support, minimum interference," and a child's learning through trial and error. This may mean a child's learning regarding:

- How much sleep is too little
- How much procrastination makes life difficult later
- How much Halloween candy makes him or her sick
- How much studying he or she needs to do to get his or her desired grade

And a million other life lessons.

The more a child digs in, the more important it is to back off as a parent, in most situations at least. Generally speaking, stronger and stronger efforts to "control" a child will not only be unsuccessful but counterproductive as it increases the adversarial dynamic.

The Beauty of Third-Party Intervention in Difficult Cases

Sometimes youth are engaged in activities at home that may be harmful to themselves and the family in a longer-term fashion, but are not acute enough to warrant a trip to the ER. Children who are using drugs, refusing to go to school, sneaking out, stealing, or engaged in other illegal and/or dangerous behavior can also benefit from the involvement of a third party. That third party might be a truancy officer, or a police officer, or a judge. This thought scares a lot of parents.

Many parents have the misconception that they are doing their children a favor by "protecting" them from the societal consequences of their behavior. Quite the contrary: they are enabling their children, turning a blind eye to their bad habits, and continuing to engage in an adversarial relationship with them. Worse, they are giving their children the message that they believe this is the best their children can do.

Rather than fruitlessly trying to cajole or force a child to go to school, it may make more sense to let him or her argue it out with a truancy officer. Let him or her try to justify drug use to a police officer. Let him or her convince a judge that sneaking out and stealing isn't a problem. We avoid an adversarial dynamic and confirm our commitment to others by "off-loading" fights. We want our group to remain an "oasis" to which our children want to return.

We often recommend that parents with children who are engaged in more chronic dangerous or illegal behavior get them involved in the court system sooner rather than later. This might mean pressing charges, or allowing charges to be pressed, or voluntarily petitioning the court for help.

Here's how the court can be our friend (and our children's, even if they don't recognize it at the time):

- It removes us from the adversarial dynamic with our child. He or she is free to argue with the judge, which usually is an approach he or she will abandon quickly.
- It opens up new, more effective ways of enforcing rules at home. Judges have power that we as parents simply do not.

- It allows us to demonstrate that we care about our children's development and welfare. We aren't getting hung up on our own anxiety or embarrassment that we have children who are behaving recklessly. We are putting our children's developmental interests ahead of our own personal image.

JOSIE AND MELANIE: MAXIMUM SUPPORT, MINIMUM INTERFERENCE

"Hello."

The squeaky, barely audible female voice emanated from Joe's office. Joe entered to investigate and found an older teenage girl communicating in a defensive crouch behind a seven-foot bookcase she dragged behind his office door to "repurpose" it (her word) for a makeshift fortress. Her name was Josie.

Another very similar-appearing girl spun around the corner.

"Are you OK? Where's Mom and Dad?" asked Melanie, apparently Josie's sister.

"Still with the doctor," came the voice from behind the fortress.

Duncan was indeed spending the second hour of the interview with the parents. They were a pleasant, young couple who, years earlier, had adopted the girls from Korea.

It did not take long for the girls to distinguish themselves as a force to be reckoned with. Impressive in their intellectual capacity and their social savvy, they were both personable, smart, good-looking girls with great parents. In short, they seemed to have every personal resource necessary for success.

But the girls had alarmed a lot of people with their behavior in recent years: bingeing and purging, superficial cutting, threatening suicide, and multiple hospitalizations each. One had just returned from the hospital for an intentional overdose.

It quickly became clear that first and foremost the twins were exhibiting serious developmental imbalances. More specifically, it became clear from the family dynamics that the girls were deeply entrenched in an abstract death match. They were competing for the attention of their loving adoptive parents by appealing to the parental instinct to protect. Each was trying to prove she was the more needy, "sicker" one.

119

It furthermore became clear that a major complicating problem in this case was the "experts" on the case. In addition to each girl being on at least a half-dozen meds, the family was working with two individual therapists and one family therapist. Moreover, somehow the family found the time to involve a gaggle of "specialists," whose individual focus varied from self-harm to eating disorders to OCD to anxiety, each providing advice to the family—and often contradicting each other.

The assembled network of providers was producing a "cure" that was worse than the disease. Well-meaning professionals were fostering the power struggle between parents and children, enabling the girls, addressing developmental imbalances with biological treatments (recall that each girl was on multiple medications), and supporting the girls' entrenched positions that they were "sick," "incapable," and not responsible for their actions.

It's the natural instinct of all caring parents to do more, to take action in the protection of their troubled children. Duncan and Joe explained their opinion to the parents: in order to help their children, they would have to do less, not more. This meant coming into direct opposition with the therapists, doctors, and prestigious clinics and hospitals who had hitherto served the girls.

Furthermore, Duncan and Joe explained that—should the parents take their advice—things were likely to get worse before they got better. This is because the usual response of kids to the elimination of excessive attention (both family and professional) is to "up the ante" and engage in increasingly provocative behavior.

To their immense credit, the parents took and adhered as best they could the advice that went against the grain of nearly all they had heard up to that point. Duncan and Joe advised them to get out of the power struggle: stop weighing the girls daily, stop trying to compel them to eat, stop doing "body checks" for cutting, stop "locking up the sharps," stop reinforcing the girls' entrenched position that they didn't have the capacity to change their behavior. They advised the parents to start responding to threats of serious harm with a trip to the ER, even if it just meant being sent home in several hours.

Well, the storm came as expected. Not surprisingly, the girls were resistant to all efforts to de-pathologize them. Duncan worked to change the medication regimen to something much more streamlined and judicious in nature. In groups, though they clearly felt loved and supported, the girls responded to challenges about their developmental imbalances in increasingly dramatic ways, and even more so at home, where they knew they had the best chance of shaking their parents' faith in the new approach. Eating-disordered behavior became more blatant, superficial cutting more common, and statements about self-harm and suicide more dramatic, resulting in multiple trips to the emergency room.

Nonetheless, Josie began coming around relatively quickly, within a couple of weeks. She showed a positive change in attitude, perspective, and behavior. She was

*just starting to see the possibilities of giving up the "sick role," becoming more inde-
pendent, and taking charge of her life.*

*Melanie, on the other hand, was not going to give up her habits so easily. She
was hospitalized shortly after for wrapping a cord around her neck (in front of her
parents). Her hospital course was rough—and made much worse by her treatment
team's being baited into a power struggle with her. She remained there for more
than a month, fighting with staff, biting and scratching herself to the point she was
frequently restrained. She was misjudged by the staff also as having a primarily biological versus developmental imbalance, and thus put on a list of new medications,
including multiple antipsychotics that caused her to gain about thirty pounds. Her
parents were beside themselves and understandably questioning once again if they
had taken the right course by following Direction's recommendations. Nevertheless,
they stuck it out.*

*About a month later, Melanie surprised hospital staff with "miraculous"
improvement "out of the blue." Duncan and Joe explained to parents that—as
expected—Melanie simply got tired of fighting. She had had it with the adversarial
dynamic. Unfortunately, her path to education was a painful one.*

*She returned to Direction a changed young woman. Duncan was able to wean
her off all but one medication for anxiety. Melanie had taken her first real step
toward giving up her bad habits.*

*This story has a happy ending. The girls have remained relatively well, aside
from a few bumps in the road, and have visited on several occasions since. Josie even
asked a Direction staff member to speak at her graduation.*

WED: A Question and Answer Session with Joe

"I've been trying to put myself out of business for thirty years.... So far, I've been an abject failure."

—Joe Walsh, LCMHC

For more than a decade, on Monday and Wednesday afternoons, Joe has taught Wholeistic Education to a parenting group. The group is free and open to the public, and we welcome your attendance. Knowing that most of you reading this book live too far away to make it, we've compiled a list of the most common questions that Joe answers each week.

1. "There are a lot of parenting books out there by other mental health practitioners. What would you say the main difference is between WED and these other approaches, like Dialectic Behavioral Therapy (DBT)?"
Control. You've heard people say that "money is the root of all evil." I say control (more precisely, the belief in and desire for control) is the root of all evil. After all, what is money but an abstract form of control? I'm not certain, but I think my view here is not too far from the Buddhist admonition against "attachment."

In my studies, it's been made clear to me. Although it's fashionable among the "experts" to denounce, often quite eloquently and even vehemently, the pursuit of control over others, and the inefficiencies of punishment—especially of our children—I can find no other organized way of parenting, outside of WED, that doesn't betray that wisdom in at least one of these two ways (and, more often, both):

A. *Failure to offer specific, clear directions, which dooms the audiences of these so-called "experts" to their default training. In our culture of "differential reinforcement" (as the pointy-headed geeks in my field call it), or "reward-and-punishment" (as us average folks call it), the default training amounts to—you guessed it—reward and punishment as a means of control! Of course—why would it be otherwise? Virtually all of us were raised in such a culture and, at least in the modern West, we are certainly immersed in it, daily.*

B. *Dependence. By promoting systems that require knowledge or even mastery of extremely complex things that are beyond many people's ability—things that may, in some cases, be unknowable—experts secure their own valued positions, at the cost of their clients.*

WED is hard, but it is simple. It provides specific guidance as to the solutions to conflict. Just add values! (We can usually offer some ideas and opinion, but ultimately you have your own values.) To be a faithful participant in WED culture, one must display a dedicated commitment to the independent wellness of all, through one's behaviors as well as one's words. The noble goal of parents and educators must be their own obsolescence. As for more specific differences between WED and other modalities of treatment (e.g., DBT), I've written essays comparing WED to these other modalities, which I hope to publish in a future volume.

2. "I can't fully implement WED at home because I'm at work all the time," or "My spouse isn't fully on board," or "The kids are at their father's every weekend," or some other logistical obstacle.

My advice is to simply do your best. It'd be great to be able to implement WED down to the smallest detail, but it is not possible. One reason is the fact that as soon as your children venture beyond the loving WED culture you've established with them, unless they are coming to Direction, they are almost certainly entering a "reward-and-punishment" culture! Adhering to WED's principles if a spouse isn't on board, or it's a split-family arrangement, can complicate things, but one parent committing to the principles of WED is better than none.

Even a single person can practice WED (as a "group of one," as it were), in that he or she can commit to the behavioral guidelines and practice of better habits. In fact, it's generally necessary to remain vigilant in our disciplined practice, to ensure we lead by example—ultimately the only effective way.

3. "When I grew up, I would never get away with what kids get away with today. Isn't this the real problem with parenting today—that kids don't respect their parents?"

Yes. Five general and virtually universally desirable "developmental goals" are sought in WED. The first is "respect," which we associate with the affirmation "I stop to see the other as me." All five are at the front of this book and also enumerated in the appendix.

It's clearly a major sign of imbalance—of miseducation—if a child doesn't respect his or her parent. But, in WED, any demonstrated lack of respect from anyone, toward anyone, is a problem.

4. "OK, so you agree kids need to respect their parents. When I grew up, we were too afraid to show disrespect. Punishment worked then. Why shouldn't we go back to it now so that our children fear us?"

I too was raised with a fear of my elders, my parents above all, as many of us were. Considering how good things turned out for my peers and me, especially in comparison to the fears we have for young people today, it's tempting to believe we should return to more of the "spare the rod" style of parenting. But I'm evermore convinced that any good childrearing results are despite the use of fear, not because of it.

I ask you, as I have asked parents over the years, is this not punishment at its root: "You have been judged as doing harm, and as a result you shall be harmed"? After all, what do you suppose is motivational about punishment? The pleasant feeling? Let's be honest, though you may have the best intentions, you are hoping that the pain of the punishment will be sufficiently motivational.

What kind of logic is that? How does it follow that someone who has done wrong, even if no doubt exists, even if the person admits it, even if they beg for punishment (not uncommon), will benefit from punishment or the threat of it? I know many of you are loving parents who are just doing whatever you are led to believe, by the most reliable sources, will be effective at promoting the best future for your children. But think of our behavioral guidelines, which delineate "nominal" rules of social interaction. If someone finds it difficult to commit to them, isn't he or she necessarily troubled, imbalanced, weak, hurting? Isn't he or she obviously even more in need of our love and support? How is it sensible to hurt someone who is already hurting?

5. "There seems to be a lot of talking and 'questions' in WED. What's wrong with 'I'm the parent, and this is how it's going to be'?"

I'm guessing, if you're reading this, you're a loving parent or educator who is desperately trying to do what's best for the child in your care. And being a parent myself, I know how much you have to do and how little time and other resources are available.

If only such talk were effective, it sure would make things a whole lot easier. Unfortunately, sometimes the quickest route is not the most direct. It may often seem like the most circuitous.

Do you remember asking your mother or father why she or he asked you to do something, only to be told, "Because I said so"? Or maybe something similar happened more recently at work. Most people are familiar with this form of control and most people have the same response, at least internally: "That's not any kind of answer that I can respect or with which I will cooperate."

When one attempts to control someone else, the reaction includes some significant, ugly mix of mindless rebellion and deadening conformity—neither of which you want for your loved ones, especially your child. Don't you really want a creative, self-possessed, confident, independent thinker, who is genuinely prosocial, cooperative, and polite?

WED defines control as a crude, hierarchical force that will inevitably confound your efforts and authority. Giving up control doesn't ensure your child will grant you authority, but it is a necessary prerequisite. Control and authority are mutually exclusive.

Sure, if you dedicate sufficient resources, you can turn your child into Pavlov's dog temporarily. But you might want to consider what that little pooch did to the good doctor's lab in his absence.

In parent groups where I teach WED's four Rs, mostly through role-plays, I insist that the second R, "remind," always takes the form of "humble questions." I often catch myself telling parents that the "magic of WED is in its humble questions." I always quickly follow up with some statement, disclaiming my belief in magic, careful not to lump myself in with the "manipulative jerks in my field who prey on parents"—those who, for the special, low price of "x" promise to "fix" your child like they are giving an antibiotic for strep throat. If it were that simple, we wouldn't need to consult "experts" in the first place!

Humble questions can "magically" transform your relationship because they access people even when they've shut you out. What I mean is that while a declarative statement often stimulates additional opposition (even more so for imperative statements), an interrogative statement automatically shifts some of a person's focus away from defense and onto the discovery of the answer.

For instance, if I say, "It's getting late—better hurry," I may just be fortifying the resistance. Without so much as a thought, a person is pre-programmed to react against the attempt to control (e.g., "I don't want to."). If I turn that into a humble question, "I notice it's almost time for you to leave [previously established in 'proactive planning'] and you're still in bed. Are you OK? Do you want some help? [if you can at that time]," the other person must turn part of his or her attention inward to determine how he or she will respond. So, even if the person chooses to lie or otherwise disrespect you, he or she is, in some part at least, in a relationship with you, and we can build from there.

It's just a fact of human nature: questions demand answers. If I tell you now that you are old, it's easy to imagine you thinking, "No I'm not," or "I know people older than me," or "You are old, too," or any number of other, reactive resistances. But, if I instead I ask, "How old are you," I'll bet not one of you failed to think of a number—even if not absolutely accurate!

6. "I've already tried everything, including the things you are talking about, and nothing works."

I hear this frequently. With all due respect, I really doubt that you have. Considering the uniqueness of WED, it's doubtful that you would have encountered anything that is fundamentally like it, let alone properly implemented it. Also, because of WED's tremendous transformational power, if you had tried it, we probably wouldn't have met.

7. "I've always told my kids that 'school comes first' in terms of their future. Are you telling me something different?"

Yes! You mean to tell me that school is even of comparable importance to relationships? If so, I must say what I've said to a room full of parents, "I indict you! I accuse you of educational malpractice!" School is for producing the academic skills necessary to acquire power and nice material things. WED takes care of "first things first." In WED we learn that one's power should not exceed one's wisdom.

No doubt, school is of immense importance, as in our culture "knowledge is power." Your children realize that! I can report that not one of my thousands of clients has rejected that truth. Though, like the old image of the young child "holding his or her breath" until he gets his or her way, many children, due to their long history of pushing their parents' buttons, will fight them on it even beyond their belief their own position.

I recommend you to John Taylor Gatto on this point. He is a veteran NYC public-school "Teacher of the Year," who is now a most eloquent, preeminent, compulsory-school critic (see the "selected sources" section at the end of this book).

With that said, I've never had a problem confirming with children that they must acquire a high school credential of some kind. It's undeniable that, in our place and time, a high school diploma or equivalent is mandatory. When you fight with your children about this (or anything, really), you are providing them an irresistible distraction. Instead of feeling the full weight and consequences of their decision to leave the group and the subsequent potential pain of their bad choices, they focus on you and your supposed "right" to punish them and all the fraudulent reasons you claim control over them. That's why one of WED's educator challenges is to "avoid adversarial dynamic."

8. "WED's behavioral guidelines are written in adult-type language. Why don't we simplify it so our kids can understand them?"

Whether due to mirror neurons, or whatever the latest theory is, children have always (and as far as we can tell, will always) be born with an intrinsic drive to imitate adults. So, by using sophisticated language, we help them learn to communicate in a sophisticated way.

Also, by not modifying the environment for some supposed lack of ability on our children's part, we signal our belief in them and our desire to team with them on a mutual project.

9. "I understand you used to be an 'anti-med' guy, yet now you seem to encourage talking to Dr. Gill about meds in some cases. Why?"

Dunc's a special guy. I've probably had more than five thousand clients in my quarter-century career. I know it's still anecdotal, but that's a lot of anecdotes, and I can honestly tell you, Dunc is unique. I know of no other doctor with comparable skill, both medically and in his ability to relate to his clients personally—especially young people.

What's more, he has proven himself to me, directly. It just seems so natural for him, especially much more for a doctor, to team up and cooperate. I know it's hard to believe, but in twelve years as business partners, with all the various stressors that normally conspire to disturb the harmony at least temporarily, and with our original, mutual suspicion, we've had exactly zero arguments. Yes, considering our striking dissimilarities, where the serious issues of business and life are concerned, we think quite similarly.

When Dunc and I first met, I was about forty years old, and aside from taking meds briefly for a hand surgery and severe sinus infection, I believe I had not taken any meds as an adult. At least I have no memory of doing so. My intention was to optimize my health, and I thought chemicals made in a factory were bound to be a net negative in that effort.

Dunc remembers correctly the disdain I felt toward the entire industry. My feeling was, and still is to some degree, that the pharmaceutical execs knew the importance of letting one's resistance and resilience develop through the "natural" processes of proper stress, and that, like in the case of big tobacco, they choose profit over public health. But while I still believe in the need and value of exercise for biological systems, I've come to realize the inevitability of that exercise occurring in the context of both our endogenous (internally produced) and exogenous (externally produced) chemistry. It seems to me now that it's all pretty much just chemistry.

Seeing how every experience modifies our internal chemistry, perhaps my focus on the "differences" between endogenous and exogenous chemicals looks for a problem where there is none.

What I learned is that the use of proper medication as prescribed by a competent doctor at the right time can be beneficial—even life-saving. I've witnessed it up close for so many years now that credibility demanded the modification of my stance. That rare competence and impeccable timing pretty much sums up my experience of Dunc's work over the years—and thus my evolution of thought on this subject.

In the pursuit of all-too-scarce answers to the question, "What's best for my child?," a loving parent can't afford to leave any stone unturned. As always, I say, "Follow your gut." But, although you may feel discouraged with the psychiatrists you've encountered, so far, keep an open mind. You may not (will not) find another Dunc, but there are docs out there who can help.

CONCLUSION

In our search for answers to helping our children overcome their imbalances, we've covered a lot of ground. We've talked about why putting ourselves out of a job as parents and treatment providers is our ultimate goal. We've differentiated between the concepts of "functioning better" versus "feeling better." We've explored both biological and developmental imbalances common to children that can be obstacles in their growth into healthy, capable adults. And we've looked at ways that good parenting, therapy, and psychiatry can help children overcome these imbalances.

Joe and I have presented our own opinions as to what constitutes good treatment. We have done our best to illustrate how psychiatry, despite its faults and limitations, can offer extremely effective treatment for those children who struggle with biological disorders. For those who started the book opposed to the idea of medication for children and teenagers, we hope we've at least given you something to think about. We've discussed how Wholeistic Education can be an effective approach to addressing children's developmental imbalances. For those who started the book attached to the idea that reward-and-punishment parenting was the only way to go, we hope we've at least aroused some curiosity about our proposed alternative.

In addition to presenting our thoughts as to what good treatment looks like, we wanted to give the reader an idea of what we think ineffective or counterproductive treatment looks like. We hope this information is useful if you decide to pursue outside help in the form of a psychiatrist or therapist for your child.

Joe and I love what we do and are passionate about our work. Many children have come through the program and have told us that, because of their experience at Direction, they would like to become therapists, psychiatrists, work with children, or otherwise enter a helping profession.

To those children out there, we would like to explicitly offer our support and have just one request:

Hurry up—we could use the help!

131

APPENDIX: DUNCAN'S TRANSLATION OF JOE'S CONCEPTUAL DIAGRAM

PHILOSOPHY: Wholeism → Organic Wisdom →
Desire and the Source of Human Behavior →
Parenting Ideal → Educational Ideal → Educator Goal →
Educational Culture → Developmental Goals → Optimal
Wellness

METHODOLOGY: Core Values →
The Behavioral Guidelines → Wholeistic Apology →
Wholeistic Leadership → Proactive Planning →
Educator Goal → Educator Objectives →
Educator Challenges → The Four Rs →
Wholeistic Tools, Programs, and Mottos

"Where's the diagram? It's the most important part—it explains everything." These words came from Joe as I showed him some of my early attempts to put WED down on paper.

This particular diagram (pictured above) has been the cause of vexation to many an individual trying to really understand Joe's way of viewing the world.

Joe has a really interesting brain. He's smart in so many different ways, and on many subjects he can share these smarts in an incredibly down-to-earth fashion. But his brain sure works differently from others, and at times, particularly on philosophical "big picture" items, I and many other of his closest friends can attest to the fact that he's really difficult to follow. Does his particular level of genius make it hard for him to articulate to others? Is it lunacy masquerading as genius? I let you, fair reader, decide for yourself. I myself have concluded it is more likely the former.

133

In these chapters, I've done my best to translate "Joe speak" into everyday language. I know that some will be lost in the translation, given both my desire for brevity and the limits of my language.

Joe says most of his philosophy of "Wholeism" had crystallized by about eighth grade. The next forty years have been spent in study to confirm those beliefs, refine his thinking, and make Wholeism his way of life. His research has included study of Eastern and Western philosophy, history, literature, and evolutionary psychology, among other fields.

Consider "The Diagram" as an outline of the theory and principles upon which WED is built.

Worst case, you'll have a window into the weird, wild world that exists in Joe Walsh's brain. Maybe that's reward enough?

In the next two chapters, we'll break The Diagram down.

THE DIAGRAM: PHILOSOPHY

PHILOSOPHY: Wholeism → Organic Wisdom →
Desire and the Source of Human Behavior → Parenting Ideal →
Educational Ideal → Educator Goal → Educational Culture →
Developmental Goals → Optimal Wellness

Right. What is this all about, anyway?

Joe believes that the most important thing to develop in one's life is one's character, and all else follows. He is furious with our school system (no, really, you should hear him go off sometime!) because it focuses on "academics" rather than character traits. Countless hours are spent on reading, writing, and arithmetic in one's formative years in school. How much time is spent in our education system on relationships? Learning to get along? Working through conflict? Handling oneself with grace? It is assumed that these are skills you'll "pick up along the way." Suffice it to say, Joe is *not* happy with the current state of affairs.

His position is that we should be spending our energy developing character traits that will maximize our ability to function as individuals and as members of society throughout life. Not that there is anything wrong with academics, but as he says it, "First things first!" (for crying out loud!).

He defines these desirable character traits as the "developmental goals." Like reading, writing, and arithmetic, they can and need to be learned through proper education.

Joe opens his diagram with his own overarching philosophy of life. Note that "Wholeistic Education" is just an aspect of a broader way of looking at the world, which he calls…

135

Wholeism

"Wholeism is the word chosen to describe the true holism of WED. The typical West-ern definition of holism rejects atomism. This is only natural. Whereas our Western paradigm is fundamentally atomistic, the two concepts—atomism and holism—are necessarily mutually exclusive. Wholeism is necessarily paradoxical. Wholeism is superdialectical. That is, it includes but is not limited by the West's typical, the-sis-antithesis-synthesis mode of thinking. It is also superhierarchical, meaning it includes but is not limited by thinking that ranks things in order of inferiority and superiority. The unique spelling of 'Wholeism' is also used to identify our proprietary, trademarked, educational service."

(Might have to break out the dictionary here.)

As far as I can figure, Wholeism is the search for understanding in the world that embraces all kinds of thought. To me, it is an expression of humil-ity and acknowledgment of the inadequacy of humans' ability to accurately describe the world around us. Because of the limitations of our brains, we should use all the models of understanding that we can. Joe and I have had ongoing arguments about whether or not the "supernatural" truly exists (you can probably guess which side we each take). To make a scientific analogy, Wholeism is essentially taking the argument about whether or not light is a particle or wave (light can behave like both, depending on circumstance) and generalizing it to include all phenomena in the world.

On the subject of human development, Wholeism starts with…

Organic Wisdom

"Organic wisdom is the essential, constitutional impetus that drives the fulfillment of needs through motivating the dynamic balance of selfish and selfless behaviors. In Western terms, it can be thought of as similar to homeostasis (but including non-physical as well as physical balancing). In Eastern terms, it can be thought of as similar to chi. Organic wisdom is both the source and goal of true education. It is consistent with a recognition of the genetic/environmental paradoxical mystery. It is superdialectical and superhierarchical."

This is the idea that all our growth comes from within—that we have an innate "wisdom" that springs forth as we develop. This originally seemed a bit hokey to me, but now I understand the usefulness of conceptualizing things this way. The idea of organic wisdom is consistent with the important principle of "following" (i.e., that "following" someone's lead is the best way to help in his or her development). It is *not* consistent with the more conventional view that we are all "empty vessels" waiting to be filled with knowledge by people smarter than ourselves. More on this important issue later. In the meantime, let's move to...

Desire and the Source of Human Behavior

"If we are to assist in the education (maturation, actualization, etc.) of others or ourselves, our first question may be, "What is the source of human behavior?" After all, parents, educators, counselors, coaches, and even friends are, on a basic level, people who assist in shaping behavior.

"Understanding first this question of human motivation helps us choose the best approaches to influence the behaviors of ourselves and others. Most importantly, it may also increase the likelihood that our actions will be consistent with our most noble aspirations.

"WED views human behavior as motivated primarily by desire. Whether desire to increase pleasure or avoid pain, physically or nonphysically, now or in the future, consciously or unconsciously, the fulfillment of desire is the cause to behavior's effect.

"We talk of three types of desires: needs, wants, and values. We define needs as physical or nonphysical desires that fulfill the requirements of nature for the wellness of the organism. Wants are defined as physical or nonphysical desires that may or may not be required by nature, and that may or may not be in the best interest of the organism. So, in addition to natural, healthy wants, wants manifest as addictions and other forms of sickness or violence. We refer to this excessive or imbalanced feeling need through the term 'neediness.'

"Accepting that desire is the source of behavior, and that desire can be healthy or unhealthy, the distinction of needs and healthy wants from unhealthy wants may be our first priority. This is where a helper, by modeling healthy relationships and providing clear reflection, can be so useful. Then, if we can accomplish this, we may follow our healthy wants and avoid our unhealthy wants—what we call discipline. Encouraging true focus on healthy wants is the function of values.

"We view values as a third type of desire. Values are powerful in that they are consciously chosen desires and a reflection of our nonconscious habits. They are the relative importance we place on things, and determine how hard we will work to achieve things. They guide us to fulfill our needs—as we understand them. Values are of immense value! They bridge the gap between nature and nurture, allowing us to choose who we will be."

Here, Joe is distinguishing between "needs" and "wants," and emphasizing the importance of developing positive values. In our quest to maintain these distinctions and develop positive values, we all can use a helping hand. When we are young, ideally we have healthy parents who guide us, representing the...

Parenting Ideal

"Parenting ideal is the concept that guides the development of WED. It is based largely on the study of philosophy, history, and natural selection. It defines the ideal behaviors for promoting education in its original sense: to raise-up, to lead-out, to nurture, within the cultural context. It is fueled by unconditional love and dynamically balances focus on both the promotion of one's evolutionary success through the improvement of one's body and "mind," and the promotion of the culture's evolutionary success through the maintenance of the culture's shared language, customs, rituals, expectations, and so on. The parenting ideal serves as a model for WED's educational ideal."

Good parenting makes for children who can distinguish needs from wants and who adopt positive values. But children aren't children forever, and some don't have ideal parents. So, who else can help us on our developmental path? Many others! Joe terms them "educators," who represent the...

Educational Ideal

"Educational ideal is the proxy or analog of the parenting ideal for educators who are not parents. It replicates and furthers the parenting ideal. And just as the parenting ideal discharges the limiting tension of the individual/group dialectic, so the educational ideal discharges the limiting tension of historic educational dialectic."

Educators are essentially parental surrogates or substitutes. They are charged with helping others pursue their...

Educational Goal

"The educator's goal is to facilitate the removal of resistance to the healing and educational power of nature (ever present as organic wisdom). It constantly strives for the balanced fulfillment of needs."

Education is fostered in an…

Educational Culture

"Wholeistic Educational Culture is produced when group members sufficiently practice the nominal rules of social interaction (i.e. the behavioral guidelines)."

This culture has been described in depth in a previous chapter. It is essentially a healthy group that promotes positive development in its members. Together, individuals in the group work toward…

Developmental Goals

The developmental goals are the culturally desired behavioral habits, specifically:

Respect—*To respect is to "re-see" or reconsider. Naturally, we recognize the differences in things as a way of making a manageable order out of our countless perceptions. However, the development of respect enables us to see beyond differences to connecting similarities. This is especially useful in human relations. On a spiritual level, we may even get to the point where it's not necessary to see differences, and all may be seen as one.*

Dignity—*When we behave in a dignified manner, we earn respect from others and from ourselves. Hierarchical, domineering, or elitist attitudes can be mistaken for dignity. WED encourages the development of dignity that reflects a balance of healthy self-esteem but at the expense of no one else.*

Responsibility—*When we lovingly respond to the needs and healthy wants of our environment and ourselves, we are acting responsibly. It's important to distinguish this from "reaction," which, although sometimes necessary, is not thoughtful and is in most cases excessively impulsive.*

Compassion—*It is not enough to simply speak of our love and concern for others. We must develop our impulse to join with others in all of the good and bad aspects of life.*

Perseverance—*Sometimes, despite our best efforts and even without apparent reason, life is difficult. In those times, we simply need to keep putting one foot in front of the other.*

The pursuit of the developmental goals brings us closer to our ultimate, larger goal, which is…

Optimal Wellness

"Optimal wellness is the greatest possible sum of health and contentment—not to be confused with 'happiness.' Also, as functionally defined, without preference for the physical or nonphysical."

Read: The ability to function better.

THE DIAGRAM: METHODOLOGY

METHODOLOGY: Core Values →
The Behavioral Guidelines → Wholeistic Apology →
Wholeistic Leadership → Proactive Planning →
Educator Goal → Educator Objectives →
Educator Challenges → The Four Rs →
Wholeistic Tools, Programs, and Mottos

Core Values

"WED's core values are the most profound, underlying ethics of the WED approach. They are following, nonviolence, Wholeistic balance, and faith."

• *Following*
  Wholeistic Education is based on a fundamental faith that the healthiest path is clearly marked for those who will follow. In the Christian Bible it is written, "Seek and ye shall find." In an Eastern tradition sympathetic with WED, one is encouraged to follow the Tao, through which "nothing is left undone." Following is akin to humble service. Following in this way causes us to question our most fundamental cultural assumptions. It demands we continuously rediscover our world ontologically, epistemologically, cosmologically, theologically, ethically, and aesthetically—that is, with regard to being, knowledge, order, spirit, right and wrong, and beauty. When following, one confronts one's often unexamined but incalculably influential assumptions regarding progress, and the relationship between individual and group. Following the direction of nature, God, or spirit, in some form, is common to the pursuit of personal fulfillment in all societies. WED encourages the thoughtful embracing of this impulse in its participants.
  This one's my favorite. Generally speaking, "following" someone's lead is the best way to help in his or her development. It's the

opposite of control. It's the second half of "maximum support, minimum interference."

- *Nonviolence*
  Another way of stating and expanding the above principle, WED avoids vio-lating the natural flow of nature (God, spirit, etc.) in all its manifestations. WED is especially sensitive to its influence on those who are vulnerable—like clients and their loved ones. Nonviolence here is not meant as pacifism, con-scientious objection, passive-resistance, asceticism, altruism, selflessness, or any other specifically defined rule set other than this: the action that contributes to the least amount of aggregate violence. This definition demands personal responsibility in the mystery of every new moment—allowing for even the most paradoxically, apparently violent responses to specific circumstances. For example, it may be perfectly consistent with WED's principle of nonviolence to purposely injure (e.g., to prevent abuse of the innocent). But any harm, any offense, however relatively minor, when a less harmful alternative is avail-able, is always inconsistent with the principle of nonviolence.

- *Dynamic balance*
  In WED, "dynamic balance" is the term that describes the result of nonviolent following. Encompassing all physical and nonphysical needs, and dynamic, as symbolized in the Chinese taijitu (yin-yang symbol), this balance is pos-sible under any circumstance. WED recognizes and celebrates this balance as manifest in respectful, dignified, responsible, compassionate, and persevering behavior. When sustained, this balanced behavior produces the greatest sum of physical and nonphysical health, and contentment—the condition known in WED as "optimal wellness."

- *Faith*
  Faith may be considered the first essential element of conscious life. All rational thought leads to a conceptual terminus at which one must decide in the absence of further evidence. WED embraces the mysterious nature of life as it embraces the ubiquitous nature of faith. In so doing, it encourages participants to take an accurate, rational measure of faith's particular manifestations in their lives, so that they may reap the benefits of faith, while avoiding the liabilities that accrue when one is controlled by rigidly held convictions (be they conscious or unconscious)—what we rightly criticize as "blind faith," "rigidity," "dog-matism," or "denial."

The Behavioral Guidelines

"Behavioral guidelines are the basic human expectations/rights that form WED practice, resulting in the maintenance of educational culture; the embodiment of WED's developmental goals; the safety required for trust, authority, liberty, volitional mutual support, triangulation of conflict, reduced ego-conflict, increased efficiency of systems, and so forth."

As discussed in a previous chapter, the behavioral guidelines form the backbone of our educational culture. They represent basic social expectations that must be met to belong to the group, and are explicated in black and white for reasons previously described. A more in-depth explanation is offered by Joe here:

"An ignoble aspect of human nature is that we are selected (through the process of biological evolution) to prefer implicit rule sets. That is, we like rules, but we like to keep them to ourselves instead of out in the open. This is because by keeping our rules hidden and not concretely explicated, we may gain a survival advantage. That is, we may be able to have the rules apply more beneficially to us than others. Naturally, because we are selected to prefer implicit rule-sets, we are also selected to be very keen at identifying others who harbor them. The identification of implicit rule sets in others induces distrust (and an adversarial dynamic). That is because we recognize it as a sign others may seek to control us, which is naturally intolerable."

Wholeistic Apology

Joe usually attaches the "Wholeistic apology" page to the guidelines when he hands them out—because we all violate the guidelines at some point or another, and it is handy to have a reference as to the best way to fess up to our errors and make things right!

Wholeistic Leadership

Also attached to the guidelines, this section describes the concept of "dynamic leadership" in WED.

Proactive Planning

Once we've established a positive educational culture by implementing the guidelines, we can move on to making plans and agreements with other group members. We work together to advance our individual and common causes, and work together to anticipate problems before they occur.

Educator Objectives

"Educator objectives define what one can do for another—model healthy relationships, provide clear reflection, and encourage true focus.

The educator objectives have been described in a previous chapter. From what Joe tells me, while working at a residential program, he was trying to come up with the best ways an individual can help another, and this is what came to him. He still has the sticky note he jotted them down on more than twenty years ago.

Educator Challenges

"Educator challenges define the educator's most difficult tasks: give up control to gain authority, neither punish nor enable imbalanced behavior, and avoid adversarial dynamic."

The Four Rs

"The four Rs are WED in action. It's WED's approach to navigating conflict or potential conflict: reflect, remind, restrict, and reintegrate."

Wholeistic Tools, Programs, and Mottos

"Wholeistic tools, programs, and mottos are the various ways we facilitate access that promote success in WED. They include the behavioral guidelines, the four Rs, Wholeistic apology, Wholeistic leadership, the personal balance inventory, Wholeistic relationships, Wholeistic nutritional guidelines, Wholeistic exercise, proactive nonviolence, Wholeistic youth sports education, virtual monastery, Wholeistic expression, and the Wholeistic education academy."

As you can see, Joe has big thoughts and big plans. These programs range from pretty much complete, to partially complete, to future aspirations, to twinkles in his eye. Hopefully we learn more about these other programs in a separate volume.

Some of WED's mottos include:

- *"Embrace all feelings, guide all behavior."*
- *"Provide clear reflection."*
- *"Encourage true focus"*
- *"Give up control to gain authority."*
- *"Avoid adversarial dynamic."*
- *"Practice the guidelines."*
- *"It's about commitment, not compliance."*

Well, there you have it: a psychiatrist's translation of "The Diagram." Consider it food for thought.

SELECTED SUPPORTING MATERIAL

Aristotle: Politics, by C. D. C. Reeves
Attachment, by John Bowlby
Civilization and Its Discontents, by Sigmund Freud
Darwin's Dangerous Idea, by Daniel C. Dennett
Dumbing Us Down, by John Taylor Gatto
Escape from Freedom, by Eric Fromm
Everyman's Talmud, by Abraham Cohen
Evolutionary Psychology, by Christopher Badcock
Experience and Education, by John Dewey
Good Natured, by Frans de Waal
Hakomi Therapy, by Ron Kurt
Man's Search for Meaning, by Viktor Frankl
Mind in Society, by L. S. Vygotsky
On Becoming a Person, by Carl Rogers
Plato: Five Dialogues, by G. M. A. Grube
Rules of Civility, by George Washington
Sexual Personae, by Camille Paglia
Summerhill, by A. S. Neill
The Art of Loving, by Erich Fromm
The Bhagavad Gita: The Song of God, by Swami Prabhavananda
The Confucian Analects, by Confucius
The Culture of Education, by Jerome Bruner
The Declaration of Independence, by Washington et al.
The Drama of the Gifted Child, by Alice Miller
The Seven Principles for Making Marriage Work, by John Gottman
The Social Contract, by Jean-Jacques Rousseau
The Tao of Pooh, by Benjamin Hoff
The Tao Te Ching: The Definitive Edition Lao Tzu, by Johnathan Star
The Theory and Practice of Group Psychotherapy, by Irvin Yalom
The Upanishads, by Max Muller
Thus Spoke Zarathustra, by Friedrich Nietzsche
The Biopsychiatric Research of Martin Teicher, by Martin Teicher

INDEX

ADHD. *See* attention-deficit hyperactive disorder (ADHD)

adolescent psychiatry. *See under* psychiatry

anorexia, 103, 119–21

antidepressants, 4–5, 32, 36. *See also* medication, psychiatry

antipsychotics, 36. *See also* medication, psychiatry

anxiety, xiv, 4, 7, 9, 19, 32, 36

anxiolytic medication, 32

apology, 73, 143. *See also* Wholeistic apology

attention-deficit hyperactive disorder (ADHD), 9, 32

behavioral guidelines (WED), 46, 71–77, 143; commitment to, 77–79; and family life, 61, 105–9; as a social code, 71–72. *See also* Wholeistic Education

behavioral problems. *See* developmental imbalances

"best practice" in psychiatry, 23–24

biological imbalances, 14–41; defined, 7–8; vs. developmental imbalance, 7–10, 11; features of, 9–10; and genetics, 10; responding to, 13–15

bipolar disorder, xiv, 5, 7, 8, 9, 19, 39

body checks, 103, 104, 120

case examples (WED), 21, 55, 67–69, 91, 119–21

child psychiatry. *See under* psychiatry

clinical depression. *See* depression

conflict resolution, 81, 94, 97. *See also* four Rs

control vs. authority, 63, 103, 123, 126

cutting, 103, 104, 119–21

delusional thinking 21

depression, 4–5, 7, 9, 19, 31, 36, 39

de Saint-Exupéry, Antoine, 109

developmental goals (WED), vii, 139–40

developmental imbalances: defined, 7–8, 45; features of, 10; responding to, 13–15

diagnosis: the diagnostic interview, 29; limitations of the diagnostic system, 27–28; of young people, 29–30. *See also* medication, psychiatry

Diagnostic and Statistical Manual (DSM), 28

dignity, 73

Direction Behavioral Health Associates: about the practice, ix–xiv, 1–15; and client agreements, 111–12;

Direction Behavioral Health Associates (*continued*): intensive outpatient program, xiv; founders' intentions, 3–6; parenting groups at, 123–29; partial hospitalization program, xiv; patient case examples, 21, 55, 67–69, 91, 119–21; and proactive planning, 109–10; and restriction, 78–79

drug abuse, x, xiv, 39, 45, 112, 116

drug addiction. *See* drug abuse

dynamic balance, 142–43

eating disorders, 103, 119–21

education and school, 6, 49, 127–28, 135

educational culture, 46

educator challenges and objectives (WED), 46, 61–65

emergency room (ER) visits for self-harm, 99–102, 116, 119–21. *See also* third-party intervention

enabling, 64, 119–21

"evidence-based" medicine, 23–24. *See also* medication, psychiatry

faith, 142

family life: adversarial dynamic, 64, 104; and the behavioral guidelines, 77–79; 105–9; and the four Rs, 105–9; healthy relationships, 61; and proactive planning, 109; and restriction, 79–80, 107–8; rules, 113–14; safety, 99–104; violence in the home, 99–102; and Wholeistic Education, 45–46, 48, 95–99, 124. *See also* parenting

family therapy. *See under* therapy

four Rs (WED), 46, 94, 106–7, 144; defined: 81–84; examples of, 85–90

Frost, Robert, 61

functioning, 3–5, 131

genetics and biological imbalances, 8, 9, 10, 23, 29, 136

Gill, Duncan, xi–xiv, 128–29

good parenting. *See under* parenting

group therapy, 45, 47–48, 52–54, 55–56, 57–59. *See also under* therapy

groups, 51–54; agreements within, 110–111; and the behavioral guidelines, 71–77, 77–79, 93; and conflict resolution, 81; group leaders, 57, 93; healthy groups, 52–54, 57–61; and proactive planning, 110; and restriction, 65, 77–80; and social codes, 71–72

habits (bad), 51–52, 104

happiness versus functioning, 3–5, 131

health and safety concerns, 73

hyperactivity, 32–33. *See also* attention-deficit hyperactive disorder (ADHD)

imbalances: behavioral, 43–131; biological, 14–41; developmental, 7; in relation to good functioning, 7–12, 131; parental response to, 13–15

inattentiveness, 32

individual therapy. *See under* therapy

Lincoln, Abraham, 105

manic episodes, 5. *See* bipolar disorder

medication: for anxiety, 19, 32, 36; as an art, 23–24; benefits of, 21, 35–36; for bipolar disorder, 8, 19; for children, 37; for depression, 19, 31, 36; and hyperactivity, 32; and (im)proper diagnoses, 8, 23–25, 27–35, 119–21; for mood instability, 19, 21, 31, 36;

myths about, 23–24, 39–41; via psychiatric treatment, 15; pros and cons, 37, 128–29; for psychosis, 19, 32, 36; resistance to, 40; for schizophrenia, 19; treatment algorithm for, 36–37. *See also* psychiatry
mood instability, 9, 19, 21, 31–32, 36
mood swings. *See* mood instability

nature vs. nurture, 9, 10, 137, 138
nonviolence, 141, 142, 144

Orwell, George, 71

parenthood. *See* parenting
parenting groups, 47, 48, 52–54, 123–29
parenting: apologizing to your children, 96–97; authority vs. control, 63, 103, 126; enabling, 104; establishing rules, 113–14; forming agreements with your children, 111–12; frequently asked questions, ix–x, 49, 110, 123–29; "good" parenting, x, 5–6, 13–14, 45, 61, 138; humble questions, 106, 126; interference, 115–16; micromanagement, 6; parenting groups, 48–49, 52–54; parenting ideal (WED), 138; punishment, 104; restriction, 79–80, 107–8; responding to imbalances, 13–15, 63–64, 99–102; third-party intervention, 116–17; and Wholeistic Education, 95–98, 105–9, 123–29
proactive planning, 109–14

psychiatry: with adult patients, 30; as an art, 23–24; basics of, 19–20; and biological symptoms, 31; child and adolescent psychiatry, 29–30, 37; diagnoses, 23–25, 27–35; and the medical field, 24–25; myths about, 23–24; 39–41; vs. neurology, 9; psychiatric treatment, 15
psychological problems. *See* developmental imbalances
psychopharmacology, 35–39. *See also* medication, psychiatry
psychosis, 19, 32, 36
punishment, 63–65, 77, 78, 84–85, 88, 89, 104, 125

reflect (four Rs), 83, 85–86
reintegrate (four Rs), 84, 89–90
remind (four Rs), 83, 86–87
restrict (four Rs). *See* restriction
respect, 73
restriction, 65, 77–80, 83–84, 87–89, 107–8
Rogers, Fred, 7, 77
rules. *See under* parenting

safety, 99–104
schizophrenia, xiv, 9, 19, 39
self-destructive behavior. *See* self-harm
self-harm, 35, 99–102, 103–4, 119–21. *See also* cutting
Shakespeare, William, 27
social codes, 71–72, 93. *See also* behavioral guidelines
social development: impairment of, 35
substance abuse, 35, 39, 137. *See also* drug abuse
successful mental health treatment, defined: 3–4
suicide and suicide attempts, 35, 99–102
superficial cutting, 103. *See also* cutting

talk therapy. *See under* therapy
therapy: benefits of, 14–15; family
    therapy, 15; group therapy, 14–15,
    45, 47–48, 52–54, 55–56, 57–59;
    individual therapy, 14;
    talk therapy, 8
three educator challenges (WED).
    See educator objectives

Walsh, Joseph, xi–xiv, 47, 71, 99,
    123–29, 134
WED. *See* Wholeistic Education
wellness (optimal), 47
Wholeistic apology, 74, 85–86, 143
Wholeistic Education (WED): advent
    of, xiv; basic principles, 45, 51–55,
    93; and the behavioral guidelines,
    71–77, 77–79, 93, 143; conceptual
    diagram of, 135–45; core
    values, 141–42; defined, 45–51;
    frequently asked questions,
    123–29; and healthy groups,
    52–54, 57–59; at home, 45–46,
    48, 95–99; implementation of,
    95–97; learning curve, 105–6;
    and logistical obstacles, 124;

methodology behind, 141–45;
    mottos, 143–44; philosophy of,
    58–59, 135–40; and restriction,
    65, 77–80, 107–8; results from,
    3–4; summary of, 93–94; and
    Wholeistic leadership, 57, 93, 143
Wholeistic Education Diagram
    of Methodology: behavioral
    guidelines, 143; core values,
    141–42; educator challenges, 144;
    educator objectives, 144; four
    Rs, 144; proactive planning,
    143–44; Wholeistic apology,
    143; Wholeistic leadership, 143;
    Wholeistic tools, programs, and
    mottos, 144–45
Wholeistic Education Diagram of
    Philosophy: desire, 137–38;
    developmental goals, 139;
    educational culture, 139;
    educational goal, 138; educational
    ideal, 138; optimal wellness, 140;
    organic wisdom, 136–37; parenting
    ideal, 138; Wholeism, 136
Wholeistic leadership, 57, 74, 75, 93, 143